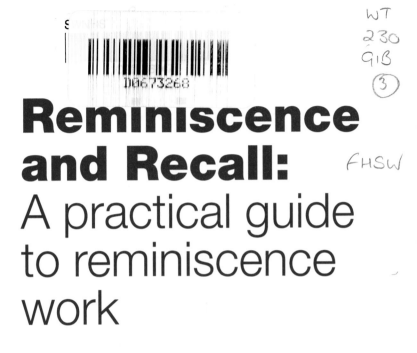

Reminiscence and Recall: FHSW
A practical guide to reminiscence work

Third edition

Faith Gibson

i

Published by
Age Concern England
1268 London Road
London SW16 4ER

First published 1994
Second edition 1998
Reprinted 2004
Third edition 2006

Editor Gillian Clarke
Production Leonie Farmer
Design and typesetting: www.Intertype.com
Printed and bound in Great Britain by Bell & Bain
Ltd, Glasgow

A catalogue record for this book is available from
the British Library.

ISBN-13: 978-0-86242-411-4
ISBN-10: 0-86242-411-9

Contents

About the author   iv
Preface   v
Acknowledgements   vii

1 Becoming old and still growing	**1**
2 What is reminiscence work?	**13**
3 Why encourage reminiscence work?	**26**
4 How to begin reminiscence work – the planning phase	**39**
5 How to lead a reminiscence group – the beginning, middle and ending phases	**71**
6 Reminiscence and life review work with individuals and couples	**100**
7 Reminiscence and oral history in community development	**129**
8 Reminiscence with people from minority ethnic groups	**139**
9 Inter-generational reminiscence work	**154**
10 Reminiscence with people who have dementia and their carers	**168**
11 Reminiscence with people who are depressed	**198**
12 Reminiscence with people with hearing, sight and speech disabilities	**210**
13 Reminiscence with people with learning disabilities	**223**
14 Reminiscence with terminally ill and bereaved people	**235**
15 Staff development, training, quality and evaluation issues	**244**

References and further reading	**255**
Appendix 1 Recording forms	**267**
Appendix 2 Resource agencies	**277**
About Age Concern	**287**
Publications from Age Concern Books	**288**
Index	**291**

About the author

Faith Gibson OBE is Emeritus Professor of Social Work, University of Ulster in Northern Ireland. She trained as a social worker and teacher in the Universities of Sydney, Queensland and Chicago, and has had wide experience as a social work practitioner, teacher and researcher.

Her reminiscence publications include numerous trigger packages, training materials, articles, research reports, chapters and books. These include *The Reminiscence Trainer's Pack* for Age Concern, *The Past in the Present: Using reminiscence in health and social care* for Health Professions Press, Baltimore, and, with Barbara Haight, *Burnside's Working with Older Adults: Group process and techniques* for Jones and Bartlett, Boston.

She writes about reminiscence and recall from wide practical experience of reminiscence work with individuals, couples and small groups, including people with dementia. She believes that skills can be learned and practice improved if reminiscence workers are willing to undertake training, read and apply ideas in practice, examine their work critically, and discuss it openly with other interested people.

Preface

For more than twenty years I have been interested in reminiscence and much involved in reminiscence work. I still continue to experience, first hand, the power of reminiscence to transcend differences of age, culture, ethnicity, gender, geography, language, nationality, professional allegiance, politics and religion. Reminiscence builds bridges between people. Through reminiscence – the sharing of memories of our personal life experience, with all their similarities and differences – we discover ourselves anew and encounter other people with enlarged understanding. We discover and rediscover the importance of relationships and recognise afresh our shared humanity with all its potential for good or ill. Far from locking us into the past, recalling and sharing memories brings new understanding, fresh perspectives and courage for facing the future.

Despite the growing international recognition that reminiscence now attracts and its developing research base, its full potential to enrich, inform, entertain, transform present limitations, and heal still remains largely under-explored and under-utilised by too many people, especially older people and those who live and work with them.

Reminiscence is both science and art, and on-going research is essential. Knowledge and understanding grow and develop each time people engaged in reminiscence critically reflect on that experience and share their ideas with others.

This handbook is a small contribution to introducing people to ideas about good practice. It is written from a developmental life course perspective to help establish sensitive, responsive, reflective, reflexive and transforming reminiscence work for the mutual benefit of people of all ages, their families, friends, volunteers and professional carers.

Faith Gibson
January 2006

Acknowledgements

In preparing this third edition I continue to be indebted to many people, both directly and indirectly, for their help and encouragement. Special thanks to all who have shared their rich recollections with me over many years, either as individuals or as members of small groups.

I have taken account of other people's research, practice experience and writings, and have drawn on ideas from many published sources. Exchanging ideas with other reminiscence practitioners and researchers has been immensely valuable but I take full responsibility for the views expressed in this handbook.

Leonie Farmer, Sue Henning and Richard Holloway at Age Concern Books, and Gillian Clarke, Alix Henley and Judith Schott have all been unfailingly helpful. Their assistance with this third edition is greatly appreciated. Much of the material from the previous editions remains relevant and has been updated and developed. New insights, recent research findings, other authors' writing and further practice experience with small reminiscence groups and individuals undertaking structured life reviews have informed the substantial changes in this edition.

I am grateful to Dorothy Atkinson, Michael Bender, Joanna Bornat, Mabel Cooper, John Killick and Pam Schweitzer for permission to quote from their publications.

I continue to be involved in different aspects of reminiscence training, practice, consultation and research. I much enjoy my association with Age Exchange and other organisations engaged in reminiscence work, the members of the European Reminiscence Network and the Northern Ireland Reminiscence Network. I owe a rich debt to family members, friends and colleagues who reminisce and who generously share their ideas and their memories with me.

Dedication

For Joyce Neill

In tribute to her years of public service and commitment to a Quaker way of life

1 Becoming old and still growing

Learning outcomes

After studying this chapter you should be able to:

- understand how best to use this handbook
- appreciate the multiple, changing needs of people throughout their lives
- realise the importance of recalling, reviewing, reconstructing and sharing memories
- be aware of why you and other people want to reminisce

Learning to listen to people's stories

Everyone has a story to tell –

If only someone will ask

If only someone will listen

This book is written especially for people who would like to know more about the importance of memory, the part played by reminiscence in later life and how to use knowledge about a person's past to enrich life in the present. It is also written for everyone who would like to explore their own memories and record them in some tangible way so that they can be shared with other people. Regardless of age, almost everyone reminisces. Even young children, adolescents and young adults reminisce but this book is primarily concerned with reminiscing by older people. It contains guidelines, suggestions rather than prescriptions or rules, to help you develop good practice in reminiscence work with individuals, families, small groups and communities.

There is much more to be learned about reminiscence work than can be covered in this introductory guide, but further reading – each chapter contains some suggestions – undertaking the application exercises and discussing reminiscence work with others will help you to make a start (Gibson 2004).

Whether you do small groupwork or individual work in a care home, hospital, club or day centre, or look after a person in their own home as a home care assistant, relative, friend or volunteer, this book should help you to develop high standards of reminiscence work.

It is important to remember three things about reminiscing. First, not everyone likes to look back and to recall the past, so you must always be guided by the person's own wishes. Even if some people are not able to express their opinion clearly, you must still make sure that reminiscence is not forced on them. People are usually able to show by their behaviour, facial and other kinds of expression, if not in words, whether or not they want to reminisce. Second, both speech and body language or non-verbal communication vary from culture to culture, so it is important not to rely on one's assumptions when working with people whose culture or heritage is different from your own. Third, if you invite a person to tell you about their past, you must have time to listen. Reminiscence is not a process to be rushed.

This handbook will help you develop the attitudes, knowledge, understanding, values and skills needed to encourage people to value themselves by valuing their past. Whether you are a paid carer or a family carer, reminiscence can enrich your relationships and enhance your caring. This means that you, as well as older people, can benefit from reminiscence work.

Try to work through this book and its application exercises with a colleague or friend; discuss your ideas with each other. Try also to find an experienced reminiscence worker who could become a supervisor, consultant or mentor; such a person can help you understand the rewards and demands associated with reminiscence work and how it affects you personally. If you have the opportunity, participate in a training course to learn about the many needs and interests of the people with whom you are involved as well as how to practise reminiscence.

It is important to attempt to put into practice, as you go along, the things you read about, because this is the way to develop skills. By trying out the ideas, you will experience first hand the infectious excitement of reminiscence work. Develop the habit of thinking back critically over each reminiscence session to help you to become a better listener and more skilled in encouraging people to tell their stories. This is also a way of taking responsibility for your own learning.

Most people find it easier to do reminiscence work if they share it with at least one other trusted person so that together you can experience its ups and downs. You will be able to discuss what happens, support and constructively criticise each other, and through this mutual help make sure that good-quality reminiscence work becomes firmly established.

Training and supervision are essential in developing reminiscence skills. Chapter 15 gives information about various reminiscence training opportunities and how training, together with critical reflection of related practice, may contribute to National Vocational Qualifications (NVQs), Scottish NVQs (SVQs) and other qualifications. For registered members of the social care workforce some of the courses mentioned could contribute towards the records of evidence and achievement designed to meet the post-registration training and learning requirements of social workers. You will need to discuss these training and development possibilities with line managers to obtain their advice, agreement and assistance. (See Chapter 15.)

Views on ageing

A good place to begin thinking about reminiscence is to examine your ideas about old age and older people. How do you regard ageing and older people? You may look at old age in two different ways: you may see people either as growing old or as being old and still growing (Bright 1997). Whichever view you hold will greatly influence how you treat older people and what you are prepared to do with them and for them. Everyone of any age is a unique individual. In some ways, people might resemble others in their age group but in many more ways each person is different. The longer people live, the more likely they are to differ from each other. So do not make the mistake of treating older people as if they were all the same. You like to be treated as a unique person – so do they.

Everyone, whatever their age, has common human needs, but the way that these needs have been met or denied throughout life will largely determine what people are like when they reach old age. Everyone is born with certain inherited characteristics and with the potential to adapt to life's experiences. Then, depending on what happens to them, and how they respond, they reach late life with some degree of resilience, acceptance, contentment and a sense of coherence, or else they may feel demoralised, depressed, anxious, critical, unhappy, disappointed and unfulfilled.

A person is very seldom all one thing or the other. Most older people display a mixture of both positive and negative characteristics, depending on their genetic makeup and life's events. Present health, economic and social circumstances, including satisfying relationships and living arrangements, also influence which characteristics and related behaviour predominate in the here and now.

Meeting the needs of older people

Age Concern's annual publication, *The Age Agenda* (Age Concern 2006), summarises the broad dimensions of current public policy, community care, legal and service delivery frameworks concerning older people in the United Kingdom. Whilst it is important to provide good physical care for older people, including comfortable, secure and warm accommodation, acceptable food, and medical and social care if required, more is needed. A strong sense of personal worth and identity, with a conviction that essential aspects of life are still under one's own control, also influences how a person ages. In helping to provide love, security and a sense of belonging, carers and care environments can help people maintain their sense of worth, self-esteem and personal identity. In many ways, both large and small, older people can be helped to feel in control. This is very important if they are to experience a sense of fulfilment, coherence and well-being until the very end of their lives.

You may ask, 'How is it possible to meet all these needs, and does it really matter if I do not?' Growing is a lifetime experience. People, whatever their age, can continue to grow and develop provided they experience the right nurturing conditions. You, but not only you, have a responsibility to help to meet older people's needs and so encourage their continued growth and development by:

- providing a warm, caring relationship;
- respecting each person as a unique individual;
- carefully listening, attending and communicating in the present;
- learning about, understanding and accepting past life history;
- encouraging people to help each other;
- making certain that people have genuine choices;
- providing opportunities for interesting, stimulating activities so that people do not have to spend their time 'busy doing nothing'.

This book aims to help you to become more competent in reaching out to older people in order to share their continuing journeys towards growth, development and personal fulfilment. It is especially concerned with recalling and reworking memories and how you might encourage older people to use reminiscence in making sense of these long journeys that they have travelled to the present. It will help you to learn about the interesting, intriguing and complex lives they have lived. It will assist you to use the past to enrich the present. As you learn about other people, you will also learn about yourself and your own life's journey.

A lifetime of experience

There is much more to older people than just what you see in the present. No one, not even the apparently most 'ordinary' person, reaches late life without a tremendous variety of good and bad, constructive and destructive, positive and negative, rewarding and unrewarding experiences behind them. Not only cats have nine lives!

Everyone has lived an intricate, interwoven series of lives. For example, as children, adolescents, students, friends, lovers, partners, spouses, parents, workers, immigrants, grandparents, widows or widowers. If you are to begin to understand why someone is as they are now, in late life, you have to know something about what has gone before and what meanings the older person attaches to their life experience. You need to learn to listen to their stories, to what is said, and also unsaid – to read the spaces between the words.

Reminiscence is a fruitful way of learning about such experience and its personal meaning. Through reminiscing, older people may be helped to review, rework and re-evaluate their lives. This process helps each person to reconstruct memories, develop new perspectives, and become more accepting of life, however it has turned out – for good or ill.

Reminiscence may be very private but usually it is a two-way process in which people share recollections with each other. This mutual process of engagement becomes a means of validating and respecting the unique individuality of each person while also recognising similar experiences. It is a way of appreciating our common humanity despite differences of age, gender, ethnicity, social background, sexual orientation, politics, religion, class, education, status, position and power.

Often it is hard for younger people, whether they are staff, family members or volunteers, to find things in common with older people. Middle-aged carers are frequently preoccupied with concerns about their own parents, their own ageing or their own children. By becoming involved in reminiscence, experiences may be shared and relationships enriched despite these many barriers.

Think of life as a tapestry. As well as looking at the 'wrong' side with all its tangles, untidiness and confusion that represents how people seem to be in the present – possibly bored, preoccupied, self-centred, frustrated, complaining, frightened or overwhelmed – look at the 'other' side. Use reminiscence to discover the rich, complex, colourful patterns of people's whole long lives. When this new view emerges, both you and they are enriched because you begin to share a journey together that will take you back to the past but will illuminate the present while taking you both forward in new, exciting and unexpected directions.

Using this guide

Ideas about reminiscence and general principles concerned with how to do reminiscence work with small groups, couples and individuals are explored in the first six chapters. Then Chapters 7–9 cover reminiscing with community groups, with people from minority ethnic groups and inter-generational reminiscence work. Chapters 10–14 deal with how to adapt the general principles of reminiscence work to meet the needs and circumstances of specific groups of people who have various disabilities or are contending with particular problems. The final chapter considers staff development and training as well as issues concerned with quality and evaluation.

This arrangement means that, although you may want to reminisce with an individual or a small group of people – for example, women who have dementia who attend a day centre – it is advisable first to read the earlier chapters before concentrating on the chapter on dementia, and so on. This sequence is important because the specific chapters build on the general knowledge already described in the early chapters. These general principles are not repeated in reference to each disability or practice situation. Moreover, because every group consists of a collection of individuals, it is also helpful to read about working with an individual even if you are sure that you intend to work only with groups. The ideas about stages or phases of work covered in Chapters 4 and 5 are equally relevant whether you are reminiscing with individuals, couples and small groups in domiciliary, day care, residential or community contexts.

Looking beyond the obvious

Age is socially constructed. This means that it is not determined by years alone but depends, to some extent at least, on the interplay between how older people see themselves, how others see them, and the continuing opportunities they have to remain involved in life, engaged in loving relationships and satisfying activities or occupations.

'Age'

Age is a quality of mind
If you have left your dreams behind
If hope is cold
If you no longer plan ahead
If your ambitions all are dead
Then you are old.
But if you make of life the best
And in your life you still have zest
If love you hold
No matter how the birthdays fly
You are not old.
  (anon)

Perhaps you already know the poem 'Kate', which illustrates how important it is to look beyond present outward appearances and to appreciate the uniqueness of each person's life. It also shows how much the writer wanted her various pathways through life, her loves and losses, to be appreciated. She wanted her story to be known – but nobody had asked her and nobody had listened. Fortunately, she found another way to preserve her story and pass it on.

'Kate – A Crabbit Old Woman'

What do you see nurse, what do you see?
What are you thinking when you're looking at me?
A crabbit old woman, not very wise,
Uncertain of habit with far away eyes,
Who dribbles her food and makes no reply
When you say in a loud voice 'I do wish you'd try'.
Who seems not to notice the things that you do,
And forever is losing a stocking or shoe,
Who tries not to help you, try as you will,
With bathing and feeding, the long day to fill.
Is that what you're thinking, is that what you see?
Then open your eyes nurse. You're not looking at me.

I'll tell you who I am as I sit here so still,
As I rise at your bidding and eat at your will.
I'm a small child of ten with a father and mother,
And brothers and sisters, who love one another.
A young girl of sixteen with wings on her feet,
Dreaming that soon now, a true love she'll meet.
A bride soon at twenty, my heart gives a leap,
Remembering the vows that I promised to keep.
At twenty-five now I have young of my own,
Who need me to build a secure happy home.

A woman of thirty, my young growing fast,
Bound to each other with ties that should last.
At forty my young ones will soon all be gone,
But my man stays beside me to see I don't mourn.
At fifty, once more babies play round my knee,
Again we know children, my loved one and me.
Dark days are upon me, my husband is dead,
I look at the future, I shudder with dread,
For my young ones are busy, making homes of their own,
And I think of the years and the love I have known.

I'm an old woman now, nature is cruel,
It's her jest to make old age look like a fool.
The body, it crumbles, grace and vigour depart,
There now is a stone where I once had a heart.
But inside this old carcass, a young girl still dwells,
And now and again my battered heart swells.
I remember the joys, I remember the pain,
And I'm loving and living life over again.

I think of the years, all too few, gone too fast,
And accept the stark fact that nothing can last.
So open your eyes, nurse, open and see,
Not a crabbit old woman, look closer, see me.

Conclusion

Reminiscence work with individuals, couples, small groups and communities is founded on the conviction that people are best placed to know and to say what is important to them. Respectful, reflective listening can assist individuals and groups to clarify and relate their own stories. The responsibility of the reminiscence worker is to enable them to engage in this process and to obtain satisfaction from so doing.

KEY POINTS

- To do effective reminiscence work you need to have a genuine interest in who people are and how they have lived their lives.

- Everyone fulfils many different roles throughout life and travels many different pathways to reach the present.

- To be an effective reminiscence worker you must enjoy reminiscing.

Application exercise

Try to imagine yourself when old and consider how the answers to the following ten questions might contribute towards your having a sense of fulfilment and well-being. If you find this too difficult, think about a specific older person you know. Try to put yourself in his or her shoes (or chair) and then ask yourself these ten questions and write down the answers:

1   Is this person in good physical and mental health?

2   Do they feel financially secure?

3   Do you know if they have experienced a major change, illness, threat, migration, dislocation, poverty, oppression, discrimination, sexual abuse, exploitation, torture, loss or bereavement, not only but particularly in the last few years?

4   Do they have regular contact with a close friend, companion or confidante?

5   Do they have opportunities for satisfying stimulation, occupation, interests and activities?

6   How well are their care needs being met?

7   Do they feel in control of their life and present circumstances?

8   What would be likely to give them great pleasure?

9   How do you think they would describe their present level of well-being?

10 What are the major values that have underpinned their life?

Further reading

Age Concern. (2006) *The Age Agenda.* London: Age Concern

Bond J and Cooper L. (2004) *Quality of Life and Older People.* Buckingham: Open University Press

Coleman PG and O'Hanlon A. (2004) *Ageing and Development: Theories and research.* London: Hodder Arnold

Gibson F. (2004) *The Past in the Present: Using reminiscence in health and social care.* Baltimore: Health Professions Press

Mandelstam M. (2005) *Community Care Practice and the Law.* London: Jessica Kingsley

2 What is reminiscence work?

Learning outcomes

After studying this chapter you should be able to:

- understand four definitions of reminiscence
- appreciate how ideas about reminiscence have evolved over time
- justify the use of the term *reminiscence work,* not *reminiscence therapy*
- appreciate the wide relevance of reminiscence work

Application exercise

How would you describe or define reminiscence?

Before reading further, write down your own ideas. Then compare them with what others have said, as quoted in this chapter. Start with your own ideas first.

Four definitions of reminiscence

Different writers have defined reminiscence in various ways. Four widely used definitions are:

- 'Reminiscence is the act or process of recalling the past.' (Butler 1963)
- 'The recalling of memories from one's personal past.' (Webster 1997)
- 'The process of thinking or telling about past experiences.' (Cappeliez, Lavallee and O'Rourke 2001)

- 'Reminiscence therapy involves the discussion of past activities, events and experiences with another person or group of people, usually with the aid of tangible prompts such as photographs, household and other familiar items from the past, music and archive sound recordings.' (Woods et al 2005)

There are a number of important characteristics to note from these definitions.

- Reminiscence may refer to a single recalled memory or to a process or series of recalled memories.
- Whilst reminiscence refers to the past, it occurs in the present and often looks to the future.
- The memories recalled relate to personal experiences or to the personal impact of public events.
- It may occur infrequently or habitually.
- It may be either a silent or a spoken process.
- It may be private or public – or a mixture of both.
- It may occur spontaneously or be triggered by some known or unknown stimulus.
- It may be opportunistic or planned.
- It may involve little or considerable evaluation of the recalled memories.

These memories may remain as private thoughts or become public by being shared in various ways, mostly, but not only, as spoken or written recollections. Memories are not static or fixed but are dynamic and are partially reconstructed, or changed, each time we recall them. Some recollections occur frequently, others are only rarely recalled. Some memories are very clear and detailed but others remain hazy, vague and general (Rubin 1996).

> **Member of a reminiscence group** *'Reminiscence makes you aware of who you are today and how you got there – I had not been willing to look at a part of my past life until I joined a reminiscence group and this made me realise I needed to face this thing, a personal thing, and I got on top of it.'*

A brief history of reminiscence work

Throughout history and in most cultures there have always been special storytellers as well as ordinary people who enjoyed passing on their experience to others by recalling the past. Some of these people wrote down their recollections whilst others relied on word of mouth. This oral passing on of traditions used to be called folklore or, more recently, oral history. (For more information about oral history, see Chapter 7.) Although such activities were accepted by some, many professional carers believed that the tendency for people to reminisce more as they grew older, to 'live in the past', was a negative side of growing older. It was to be deplored, not valued, to be discouraged, not encouraged.

It is only in the last 40–50 years that health and social care professionals have slowly begun to realise the importance to older people of being able to look back, to recall the past and to share their recollections with others. Reminiscence, an ordinary everyday activity, used by most people throughout their lives, is increasingly valued and is being widely used for educational, recreational, social and therapeutic purposes.

Increasingly, writers emphasise the importance of understanding why people of all ages talk about the past and why we benefit from telling our unique stories and having them heard by other people. In the mid-1970s, Mick Kemp (1978), an architect by training, when working for the Department of Health and Social Security in London studied residential institutions for older people. He realised that, unlike older people at large, nobody was talking about their past. There was a very real belief among caring professionals that it was wrong to encourage reminiscence, as it interfered with a proper grip on today's reality.

Kemp persuaded Gordon Langley, a psychiatrist, and a small team of artists and psychologists to help him develop a reminiscence aid. Help the Aged, who in 1981, published the three-part tape/slide package *Recall*, carried Kemp's pioneering work forward. This audio-visual package dramatically stimulated the extensive development of reminiscence because busy staff in care homes, hospitals and day centres now had a readily available working tool. Occupational therapists, psychiatric nurses, activity nurses and diversional therapists, among others, quickly recognised that reminiscence activities provided widely acceptable social and intellectual stimulation. Many other more local contemporary aids similar to *Recall* have been produced in the intervening years and many different kinds of paid and unpaid carers now use reminiscence in countless ways in their day-to-day work.

A number of US clinicians and researchers were already writing about the many different facets and functions of reminiscence before *Recall* was published. Their work provided the early theoretical underpinning for the British work that was stimulated by the publication of *Recall*. In the years since, interest has spread to many other parts of the world, including Australia, Canada, Japan and Europe. The reminiscence training, theatre, exhibitions, conferences and publishing promoted by Age Exchange Reminiscence Centre in Blackheath, London, have had a major impact on the development of reminiscence work worldwide. Initiated by Age Exchange, the European Reminiscence Network engages in trans-national training, action research and development projects. Its reminiscence theatre festivals, touring exhibitions and international conferences provide fruitful exchange between community artists, health and social care professionals, researchers, writers, library and museum staff, older people and volunteers. The International Institute of Reminiscence and Life Review provides a North American focus for the promotion and development of reminiscence research, publications and practice, and its biennial conferences bring together practitioners and researchers from many professions, including narrative and clinical psychologists, health workers, social workers and family historians.

The increasing popularity of therapeutic reminiscence work has also coincided with a growing interest in oral history, local history and family history. Historians are interested in making an accurate record of the past; they are less interested in the processes of remembering but have become increasingly aware of the effect on interviewer and informant of the interview experience. They use focused oral evidence in seeking to understand and interpret history. For them the outcome, most often an audiotape and transcript, is central. Because many reminiscence groups, although primarily interested in providing personal fulfilment, communication and social stimulation, are also interested in producing a record of shared collective memories, it is not always easy to distinguish precisely between reminiscence work and oral history.

In oral history and folklore there are traditions of collecting and recording memories, both with individuals and in groups, but the emphasis until recently has been more on recording individuals. Most reminiscence work is undertaken in small groups but individual work, often called 'life history', 'life story' work or 'life review', has also grown in popularity. As Joanna Bornat (1989), an oral historian and sociologist, suggested, reminiscence work, like oral history, can be thought of as a democratisation process – of giving people their place. In the health and social care services, reminiscence groupwork and individual life story work are now undertaken in many hospitals, care homes and day centres. Community arts organisations, community development agencies, voluntary community and social agencies, housing associations, museums, libraries, schools and colleges are actively pursuing reminiscence and allied activities either with mixed aged groups or with older people.

With increasing numbers of frail older people continuing to live at home, domiciliary carers also need to understand about the importance of reminiscence because they have many spontaneous opportunities to reminisce in their ordinary conversation with older people or while undertaking other care tasks. Sometimes they may also want to use planned reminiscence as part of a package of care to enrich communication, lessen isolation and provide constructive occupation. Family carers also benefit by learning to use reminiscence but it is not always easy for them to find the time and energy required. More might be encouraged to do so if they were assisted by trained volunteers. The increasing numbers of frail older people living alone could also benefit from regular visits by reminiscence volunteers, and some are beginning to have such opportunities.

Recognising the importance of the past has liberated both older people and their professional and family carers. People are now free to remember. You as a carer are free to encourage them and to share in remembering. As Rose Dobrof (1984, page 17), a social worker, said:

> 'In a profound sense, Butler's writings liberated both the old and the nurses, doctors and social workers; the old were free to remember, to regret, to look back reflectively at the past and try to understand it. And we were free to listen and to treat rememberers and remembrances with the respect they deserved.'

Reminiscence is not limited to older people although they are the major focus of this book. Depending upon their life circumstances and the challenges they face, children, adolescents and adults of all ages may benefit from reviewing their past lives and present circumstances in order to gain courage and confidence to face the future.

Major characteristics of reminiscence

Different characteristics of reminiscence work can be distinguished. It may be a private or a public process. It may be undertaken with an individual on their own, by a worker with two other people, or it may be a much more public process in which memories are shared with others in a small group with each person contributing their recollections.

Reminiscence is usually cumulative, which means that one memory leads on to another. One person's shared recollections frequently stimulate associated recollections in others, which in turn result in more detail being recalled and related stories being recounted.

Both private and public reminiscence may be spontaneous, unintended or memories, and talk about memories may be purposely and deliberately encouraged. Whether recall is spontaneous or prompted may influence the memories recalled, whether they relate to the distant or the recent past, to recollection of knowledge or to autobiographical life experience. This handbook is primarily concerned with encouraging good practice in prompted or planned recall about personal life experience but also seeks to widen understanding about the value of responding to spontaneous recall.

Reminiscence may be internal, something that goes on inside a person, or it may be externalised. By translating images into speech, writing, poetry, drawing, painting, drama, mime, music, dance or some other communication medium, the recollections have the potential to be shared with others (Gibson 2004). This process of sharing enriches the experience for both teller and listener, provided that the storyteller experiences the listener as being genuinely interested and totally without patronising condescension.

In the telling and retelling, the detail of a memory subtly alters. Both the context and the interaction between the teller and the listener influence the story. It does not matter if the details change. Think of recalling memories as being more like painting than photography. Each time a picture is worked on, changes of light, mood and other circumstances will influence what is painted. Recalled memories are somewhat similar. Whilst the major characteristics or core remain recognisable, the fine details alter, reflecting differences of emphasis, mood, memory and interpretation. Our recollections will always be coloured by such personal changing interpretation because, as Pear (1922) suggested, 'The mind never photographs. It paints pictures' and these mind pictures come wrapped in emotion.

Most people enjoy reminiscence, but remember that reminiscence does not suit everyone and it must never be hurried. You must never urge people to reminiscence against their better judgement. Always respect their wishes. People of all ages reminisce, not just older people. There is a widely held belief that older people reminisce more than younger people. This is probably not true for spontaneous recall for older people who are living active, independent, fulfilling lives. Recalling memories about the distant, rather than the recent, past possibly increases in older people whose present lives are bleak or boring, where nothing happens worth recounting or where memories are being purposely prompted by the use of aids, props or triggers.

Not all reminiscence can be about happy memories because no person's life consists only of 'good old days'. Reminiscence recalls past pain as well as past happiness, past loss as well as past joys. Reminiscence is not about sentimental, nostalgic 'trips down memory lane' where the present is compared unfavourably and is tinged with regret for times past.

On the contrary, the modern reminiscence movement is primarily con-cerned with using recollection of past experience as a tool for coping in the present and anticipating the future. It is a dynamic not a static process, which brings the past into the present and which constructs and reconstructs a newer version of recalled memories. If you want to do reminiscence work, you must be prepared for, and able to cope with, whatever kinds of recollections and their associated emotions that emerge. More guidance about this is given in Chapter 11.

Reminiscence therapy or reminiscence work?

This book does not talk about 'reminiscence therapy' although some writers, especially those employed in medical settings, do. Instead, the term 'reminiscence work' is preferred. This is because reminiscence is valued as a mutual process, a shared journey. People regardless of age who reminisce are not necessarily ill – although some may happen to be – and awaiting treatment by expert reminiscence professionals, as the word 'therapy' implies. Rather, they are the teachers, informants, authorities and repositories of invaluable information about their own past lives.

The task of a reminiscence worker is to encourage and assist people to share their life-long experience with you and with others, here and now, in the present. Although talking about the past, people are communicating in the present. In the process you too will be enriched because you too are a participant, not an aloof, remote observer. Older people, care staff, volunteers and family members can all benefit from using this ordinary everyday process. In many ways, reminiscence is therapeutic, even though it is not strictly a therapy.

Reminiscence work includes many different approaches, depending on the level of knowledge, skill, confidence and experience of the people who use it. It is not a set of precisely defined and rigorously tested techniques. There is no one universally agreed definition. Instead, it is a loose collection of ideas resulting in varied approaches, activities and practices that differ according to the specific objectives of the work, who does it and where it takes place.

Reminiscence groupwork, individual life history work and structured life review described in this handbook all differ from large recreational and social activities. These may include trips to museums, tea dances, fashion shows, mock weddings, old-time musical functions, sing-alongs, theatre and film shows, and usually involve much larger numbers of people. Within such activities, however, there will be many opportunities for spontaneous reminiscence, or these large events may be used as springboards for more intimate reminiscence work at a later time.

Different types of reminiscence

In hospitals and care homes where people live in groups, and in day centres, reminiscence is usually undertaken as a small group activity. Some people, however, are much more suited to individual work and it is a mistake to assume that because people live in groups they should only be involved in groupwork.

It is helpful to distinguish between general or simple, and specific or specialised reminiscence work. *General* work refers to well-planned work that uses open-ended questions or various triggers to stimulate recall on topics likely to interest the participants and unlikely, as best as can be judged, to stimulate painful, traumatic or long-buried memories. This type of simple reminiscence usually employs easily available materials, or triggers, to encourage recall of readily accessible memories. It is likely to emphasise sociability, educational and recreational objectives. It is more likely, but not always, to be undertaken in a group.

An example is a group of eight women in a care home who met with two staff members for ten weekly sessions to read aloud from library books, to look at photographs and newspaper cuttings about women's work and to share memories about their working and domestic lives.

Specific reminiscence is more likely, but not invariably, to be undertaken with individuals or in small formed groups with closed membership. It requires carefully selected participants, clearly defined objectives and careful, focused, planned use of triggers designed to be of immediate relevance to the people concerned. It uses materials either owned by or closely associated with the participants' known past interests and is particularly, but not only, relevant to individuals who have dementia or are demoralised, depressed or disturbed. The objectives of the work are likely to be to increase self-understanding and self-acceptance, to enhance self-esteem, to confirm personal identity, or possibly to achieve behavioural change. It will encourage personal life review and self-evaluation. Structured life reviews with an individual or guided autobiographical writing in a group are examples of specific work. Some writers also like to distinguish other types of reminiscence; for example, integrative and instrumental reminiscence. (See Chapters 3 and 6.)

An example is a man with early dementia attending a day centre. He is unhappy, aggressive towards other members and very isolated. A worker spends time twice weekly with him to talk about his earlier family life, work and retirement. Together they write a life history and illustrate his story with photographs obtained from his family.

Depending on people's circumstances and needs, either simple or specific work may be more appropriate. Each approach requires skilled workers prepared to undertake careful planning, preparation, reflection on and evaluation of the work undertaken. Both approaches can considerably improve people's quality of life by enhancing communication and building relationships. Before starting, it is important to decide what kind of reminiscence work may be more appropriate where you work and what best suits the needs and interests of the people you wish to involve.

Who should undertake reminiscence work?

This is an important question because some professionals may wish to claim reminiscence as their exclusive territory. Reminiscence is not the monopoly of any one profession. It is not necessarily the monopoly of any profession. Many different people with assorted backgrounds employed in various types of organisations do reminiscence work. These include health and social care staff in residential care, day care, nursing, social work, clinical psychology, occupational therapy, speech therapy, diversional and activity therapy as well as oral historians, artists, librarians and museum staff. Volunteers or people with few recognised qualifications also do reminiscence work. Inter-generational work frequently involves teachers or youth workers. Family carers, too, are increasingly being encouraged to appreciate and to use the rich possibilities of reminiscence.

Attitudes, values, knowledge and skills are more important than any particular professional background. Reminiscence work is based on respect for each person's unique individuality; it recognises the inter-dependence of people within relationships and communities. Skills can be learned, and those needed for effective reminiscence work include:

- active listening – 'listening with the third ear';
- empathising – sharing another's world without losing hold of your own;
- attending – being available to people;
- relating sensitively – not being a bull in a china shop;
- being non-judgemental – accepting people as they are;
- not being frightened by the expression of painful emotions;
- being able to enjoy reminiscence and be interested in the past;
- being disciplined, but willing to share your own reminiscences;
- being able to reflect upon and to criticise your own work;
- being able to accept and offer criticism.

Conclusion

Reminiscence and life review mean different things to different people. This everyday common process is more complex than may first appear. Without a widely accepted standard definition it is not uncommon for people to use the terms 'reminiscence' and 'life review' in different ways. So before commencing reminiscence work it is important for you to be clear about what you mean and what you hope to achieve through reminiscence. Each time people recount stories of their personal life experience, the accounts will be influenced by variations in the recall process, present mood and circumstances and how the storyteller perceives the reaction of the listener. For this to be a satisfying experience the storyteller must feel respected and listened to and that the story being told is understood, believed or validated.

KEY POINTS

■ Reminiscence and recall indicate mental health, not mental ill-health.

■ Some aspects of reminiscence resemble oral history.

■ Reminiscence is more concerned with inter-personal processes than with achieving factually accurate history or tangible products.

■ Not everyone wants to reminisce. Personal choice must be respected.

■ Reminiscence is undertaken with individuals, pairs or small groups.

■ Memories have many facets, which may alter in the telling.

■ Some memories may be very painful to tell and distressing to hear.

■ Reminiscence is a process that must not be rushed.

■ Reminiscence skills need to be learned through training, practice, reading, supervision and reflection.

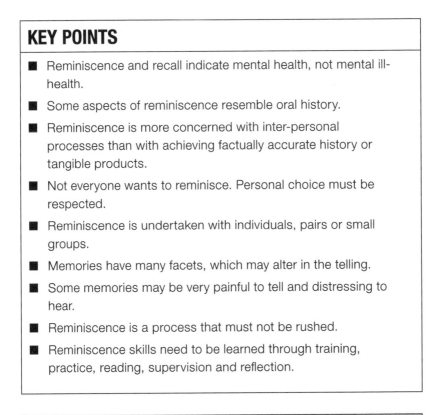

Application exercise

Ask yourself the following two questions. Write down your answers. Try to find someone you trust and with whom you feel comfortable so that you can discuss your answers with them.

1 What aspects of reminiscence work appeal to me?

2 What aspects of reminiscence work worry me?

Further reading

Bornat J (Ed). (1994) *Reminiscence Reviewed: Evaluation, achievements and perspectives.* Buckingham: Open University

Haight BK and Webster JD (Eds). (1995) *The Art and Science of Reminiscence: Theory, research, methods and applications.* Washington, DC: Taylor and Francis

Webster JD and Haight BK (Eds). (2002) *Critical Advances in Reminiscence Work: From theory to application.* New York: Springer-Verlag

3 Why encourage reminiscence work?

Learning outcomes

After studying this chapter you should be able to:

- list ten reasons for doing reminiscence work with individuals, families, small groups and communities
- understand Webster's classification of the functions of reminiscence
- explain why it is important to set objectives for planned reminiscence work
- recognise different attitudes to reminiscence and different styles of reminiscing

Application exercise

Why do you think reminiscence work might be important? Begin by writing down as many reasons as you can. If possible, get a colleague to do the same and then discuss your reasons with each other.

Ten reasons for doing reminiscence work

There are many different reasons why people reminisce. These vary over time according to the needs of each person involved and the place or context in which the reminiscence work is undertaken.

1 Reminiscence makes connections between a person's past, present and future

Our remembered past sheds light on the present and prepares us for facing an unknown future. It helps with problem-solving. By looking back we are able to draw on evidence of past coping; we are encouraged in times present; and dare to hope we shall cope in the future.

Most people find being in hospital or moving into a care home or sheltered dwelling, beginning to attend a day centre, or facing up to any new experience involving changed circumstances and meeting strangers, a daunting experience. Remember how you feel when you are 'new'. Put yourself in the shoes of older people who may have lost good health, independence, their own home, significant people, familiar places and possessions, and the routines of a lifetime. Reminiscence can help ease the anxiety of such major life events. If you can assist people confronted by such challenges to draw on their past experience of coping and surviving, they may be greatly encouraged in facing up to the inevitable demands of present and future changes.

2 Reminiscence encourages sociability and opens up new relationships

At a stage in people's lives when their social networks – meaning the significant people to whom each is connected – are probably shrinking because of death or changes in living arrangements, reminiscence may open up new relationships. It may help people to make new friends, or rediscover old friends, because it may help them see that other people have had similar experiences. They discover common ground or come to better understand the reasons for people being different. Talking about the past becomes a rich means of talking in the present, of discovering new resources in themselves and in each other.

Even if people live surrounded by others, in homes or hospitals, you must not assume that this means they have close, supportive, warm relationships. Some will but others will feel isolated, lonely and unhappy. They may be grieving for lost places, lost people and lost independence. They may be struggling with coming to terms with how to lead private lives in public places. The challenge for staff is how to help residents reconcile their need for personal privacy with their need for significant relationships. Both needs require attention.

Joining a small reminiscence group may help solve this dilemma. Here the person can share those parts of their lives that they choose to talk about. They remain in control of what they say about themselves but the leader enables them to talk in their own way and in their own time. As they begin to trust the other group members they will feel more confident about moving from superficial conversation to talking about significant experiences. In sharing both pain and pleasure, hard times and good times, each person learns to accept themselves and others, and new relationships emerge.

This process of growing towards others through sharing deeply felt emotions is not limited to groups. It also applies to reminiscence work with individuals. The possibilities, however, are enlarged and multiplied through group experience. Here each member has the potential for becoming a resource to every other member while at the same time benefiting themselves. The richness lies in both giving and receiving.

> **Care assistant** *'We use reminiscence groups as a means of introducing a new resident and to help them feel at home with us. Reminiscence helps them find other people from the same neighbourhood with similar backgrounds to whom they can talk in familiar ways. It gets them over the strangeness.'*

3 Reminiscence confirms a sense of unique identity and encourages feelings of self-worth

A strong feeling of personal identity, of knowing who you are, gradually emerges in adolescence and young adulthood. This sense of identity is important at every age. It helps us to remain in control of our own lives and not to be overcome by the pressures that allow us to be treated as if we were worthless human beings or just the same as everyone else.

Some people, as they grow older, feel they are no longer valued by others, and some find it difficult to value themselves. All too easily they accept the negative ideas around them, diminishing their own significance and achievements, allowing themselves to be marginalised. Such threats to self-esteem may be even greater for older people who have experienced earlier discrimination or racism. By showing a genuine interest in the lives people have lived, by reminiscing, you may be able to help rekindle or reinforce a sense of uniqueness, of personal identity and self-worth. In this way you will encourage people to value themselves in the present and to remain more in control of their own lives.

4 Reminiscence assists the process of life review

The term 'life review' is used loosely as a general term and also in a more technical way. In general, many people as they grow older become increasingly aware of past experiences, especially painful, difficult, unfinished business or unresolved conflicts. Everyone has particular tasks to work on at different stages in their lives. The task or challenge that faces older people is to come to terms with life as it has turned out – for good or ill. Some become increasingly aware of trying to review, resolve, reorganise, reintegrate and tidy up their past experience in the face of encroaching age and approaching death. Dealing with the past becomes a part of finding meaning in life and preparing for death (see Chapter 14).

It does seem that for many, but not all, older people, if they can be helped to take a second look at their past, to 'put their house in order', they develop a kindlier view of themselves. You can help them in this process of life review by affirming that their life has been significant. In becoming easier on themselves, many become easier on others around them. Dealing with the past makes life in the present more understandable, more bearable.

5 Reminiscence challenges the distribution of power

Reminiscence can be a most effective tool for improving communication and empathic understanding. By telling their stories, people reach out to others while reaching deep into themselves. Telling the stories of life creates, sustains and alters relationships.

In almost all institutions (and in families, too) there is a pecking order. Everybody, staff member, family member and resident alike, has their 'place'. Staff are always more powerful than residents. People with dementia are especially likely to experience a loss of significance or importance: within their own families, in communities and in health and care establishments. Reminiscence work, however, in which residents, family members, volunteers and paid carers share experiences will help restore a sense of personal significance. In this sense reminiscence work can empower older people and others who feel disregarded.

In understanding a person's past, it is easier to understand their present behaviour – even troubling and troubled behaviour. People become more finely tuned to each other's needs, more accepting of them and more able to reach out to each other. By reminiscing together, people learn to trust each other more as people and become less preoccupied with position, power and protocol. In this sense, reminiscence can have far-reaching, radical implications and consequently not everyone welcomes it.

6 Reminiscence encourages communication and assists staff development

When you have only recently met someone, it is nearly impossible to understand why he or she is as they are now. Everyone travels many journeys to reach the present and some of these journeys are harder than others. Past experience leaves its mark. If, by listening to people reminisce, you come to learn about these different journeys, you will better understand the traveller in the present. Because you see the older person differently, you will treat them differently. When you appreciate each person as a unique individual your understanding is increased; your sympathies are enlarged. You can help celebrate and value the heroism of lives remembered. If, on the other hand, the reminiscence reveals suffering caused to others in the past, you will need to distinguish between accepting the person but not accepting their past behaviour. You will need to listen to their story, if possible help them to find forgiveness, make restitution, and resolve or integrate their painful memories.

> *Manager of a care home* '*I never understood why Hugh was so difficult, why he hated being here so much, until I heard him talk about his childhood. Now I see him differently, I understand him more and we have something to talk to each other about.*'

7 Reminiscence aids assessment of present functioning and informs care plans

If you consider only how a person is in the present, it is like taking a single snapshot instead of looking through a whole photograph album. It is not a fair way to assess a person's present capacities. You cannot understand them now without knowing what they used to be like, what they used to be able to do, and liked to do, what values influenced them, and what they desired for themselves and their families. Their history suggests what they may still be able to do and what might still interest them, given half a chance. Reminiscence helps fill out the detail of a person's life history and helps illuminate the present. It is vital that assessments and care plans are based on all relevant information, both past and present, because judgements made by professionals can have profound consequences for influencing ill-being or well-being of people receiving health and social care services.

In some care homes, reminiscence with a key worker may be an established way of assisting assessment, helping newcomers settle and developing a care plan. Life stories reveal how different people think about their own lives and what meanings they attach to life. The process of gathering a life story helps the carer to grasp the essence of the other person and understand how they view their present changed circumstances in the light of their life-long values and experience.

8 Reminiscence reverses the gift relationship through transmitting knowledge and values and by bearing witness

Those who have lived history are its best teachers. Bearing witness is important to many people as they grow older, and reminiscence may be described as seeing and seeing again, of telling and telling again.

Older people are irreplaceable sources of historical knowledge and, given encouragement, many are prepared to share their experience and wisdom with younger people. Instead of being passive recipients of others' caring, of having things done for them and to them, through reminiscence they are able to move to the centre of the stage. As soon as older people become the teachers, their carers become the learners.

In letting an older person become the authority, you become the student. They become the giver while you become the receiver. So reminiscence connects the storyteller to their own earlier life, to their contemporaries and to other generations.

Each time an older person dies, history dies with them. A book is lost. This loss is felt most acutely by close family members. Encouraging families to discover and preserve their family history before it is too late can lead to great mutual satisfaction and shared pleasure between the generations in the present.

> **Bereaved family carer** *'Why did I leave it so late? I always meant to get Mum to tell me about the family but I never got around to asking her. When I was younger I was bored by her stories. When I was older I was too busy to bother. Now she's gone and we've lost her and we've lost the family history too.'*

How much more positive is this daughter's recollection?

> *'For the last two years I have been doing Mother's family tree. This has been a great interest for her as she was a great storyteller and had, right up to her death, an excellent memory. Reminiscence for her was a trip from Portadown where she grew up right through Ireland to all the towns she had lived in. They moved every five years because of my father's job as a Methodist minister, so she had a lot to tell.'*

If we learn to listen to people remembering and remember ourselves, we capture the past. If we tell someone else, record or write down the recollections, we help to preserve the past and transmit the culture. This applies as much to domestic history as to national history. One is the record of so-called ordinary people telling about their ordinary lives. The other concerns national events that people may have witnessed, or the times they lived through when such events occurred. Bornat (1989) writes about reminiscence as a social movement because reminiscence gives a voice to those not usually thought of as opinion formers. It provides raw material for oral history that Paul Thompson (2000) persuasively argues has now become a respected part of historical studies.

9 Reminiscence contributes to social inclusion and community development

Many neighbourhoods and communities lack a sense of social cohesion and shared values, different groups within them experiencing isolation, marginalisation and discrimination. Reminiscence and oral history groups can provide a focal point for bringing minority groups together, lessening mutual suspicion and promoting shared understandings.

As well as stressing the importance of recognising the unique individuality of each person, it is also essential to foster relationships within communities and between groups of citizens who may differ in age, ethnicity, religion, culture, language and politics. Exchanging personal and communal histories is one way of identifying what hopes and aspirations people have in common, of fostering friendships and building cohesive, responsive services. People do not have to remain captives to history and heritage; difference can be appreciated and celebrated and become a force for good rather than division. The history and often-repetitive character of community conflict and suspicion can be discussed and re-evaluated. Reminiscence undertaken within a community development framework is more often described as oral history but its objectives and many of the methods used closely resemble reminiscence work.

10 Reminiscence and related activities are relatively easy to undertake, economical, low risk and are widely enjoyed

Talking about the past evokes an immediate response in many people. This does not mean that all reminiscence is happy. Some recollections will be happy, others sad. Not everyone wants to reminisce. Respect any reticence or reluctance. Some people can only keep the painful past in its place by ignoring it. Others may be so taken up with living in the present and thinking about the future that they have no time or desire to think about the past.

Henley and Schott (2004, page 184) caution: 'It is unhelpful to assume that talking is always a good thing, and intrusive to expect it of everyone. For some people, the last thing they want to do, or are able to do, is to talk about their feelings.'

Most of us, however, get enormous satisfaction from recalling the past and sharing the personal meanings that we attach to our experience with empathetic, appreciative listeners. For many people and their carers reminiscence, especially in groups, gives intense pleasure, excitement and enlightenment. For others it is a diversion, a means of reducing boredom, of passing the time. For most it is a constructive occupation that often leads on to many other related creative activities (Craig 2005).

Webster's classification of reminiscence functions

Jeffrey Webster (1997, page 140), a psychologist, has developed a Reminiscence Functions Scale (RFS) from which he derived eight separate factors representing the main functions of reminiscence:

- boredom reduction – having something to do;
- death preparation – valuing the life lived and becoming less fearful of death;
- identity – discovering and better understanding a sense of who we are;
- problem-solving – drawing on strengths and experience from the past for coping in the present;
- conversation – rediscovering common bonds between old and new friends;
- intimacy maintenance – remembering personally significant people who are no longer present;
- bitterness revival – sustaining memories of old hurts and justifying negative thoughts and emotions;
- teaching/informing – teaching younger people, including family members, about values and history.

Cappeliez and O'Rourke (2002), building on earlier work of Watt and Wong (1990) and Wong and Watt (1991) together with Webster's work, grouped Webster's eight functions under four headings as follows:

- Intra-personal functions done primarily for the benefit of the person – integrative, escapist, obsessive and death preparation.

- Inter-personal functions that primarily serve a social function by connecting the person with others – narrative storytelling and intimacy maintenance.

- Problem-solving – an instrumental function designed to assist present coping.

- Transmissive – to provide an instructive story consisting of experience and knowledge for the benefit of others and for representing oneself as competent.

Different attitudes to reminiscence and different styles of reminiscing

Peter Coleman (1986), a psychologist, identified four different attitudes held by people to reminiscence and how these attitudes influenced their morale. Table 3.1, which is based on his research findings, confirms that reminiscence does not suit everyone.

Table 3.1 Morale and types of reminiscers

1 Reminiscers	People who value memories of the past	High morale
2 Reminiscers	People troubled by memories of the past	Low morale
3 Non-reminiscers	People who see no point in reminiscing	High morale
4 Non-reminiscers	People who avoid reminiscing because of the contrast between their past and present	Low morale

Source: Adapted from Coleman (1986, page 36)

It is very important to try to understand people's perspective on their life story. For the first group of people identified in Table 3.1, who reminisce readily, their memories are a source of strength which they and you can use as a resource in the face of present difficulties. If faced with problems, a reminder that they have coped in the past may encourage such people to draw on evidence of past coping and to use this experience to overcome present problems. The past becomes a resource in the present.

The second group brood on their memories, feeling regretful and sad. You will need to try to understand how rational or irrational such regrets are. Counselling may help these people to view their past and their understanding of it somewhat differently. There are people who have very good reasons for feeling guilty about their past. They may welcome encouragement and assistance to make amends and to seek to be reconciled. If this is not possible – for example, if the person they have wronged or ill-treated is inaccessible, perhaps dead – they may be helped by talking with a pastor, priest or faith leader or a professional counsellor to assist them to move from a sense of guilt to a sense of forgiveness, acceptance, peace and reconciliation.

The third group should be helped to get on with the things they consider are important to them here and now. They should not be forced to contemplate their past. If they are 'doers', your task is to help them get on with doing whatever is currently important to them.

The fourth group say their past lives were happy but reminiscence makes them sad when they do not need to be, so they avoid thinking and talking about the past. Unless these people can come to terms with the changes and loss in their lives, they are likely to remain depressed or demoralised.

Prem Fry (1995), a psychologist, suggested that people have different styles of reminiscing. As they tell their life story, the careful listener comes to understand whether the teller uses reminiscence in an affirming, a negative or a despairing way. People with an affirming style accept both positive and negative life experiences. They are able to face conflicts or problems and to feel reasonably hopeful that the difficulties can be resolved. They have a sense of wholeness or coherence about their lives.

People with a negative style of reminiscing present life as gentle and pleasant. They ignore or play down or wall off painful or traumatic experience, and often recall public rather than personal experience as a means of distancing themselves from the impact of talking about their intimate past; they play it safe.

A despairing style means that the person is painfully aware of, and probably preoccupied with, unresolved conflicts and past and present negative experiences. These feelings emerge as a lack of fulfilment, pain and disappointment that the person seems unable to repress, deny or grow beyond.

So you can see that although reminiscence is a very common everyday experience, engaged in by most people from time to time, it is not as simple as it first seems. The importance of being able to remember is summed up by McConkey (1997), a writer: 'Memory is responsible for our identity: it is the faculty whereby we perceive connections between past and present, thus enabling us to make sense of our surroundings; it underlies our creative achievements.'

KEY POINTS

- The functions served by reminiscence differ from person to person and for each person over time.

- Not all the identified functions apply to everyone or to the same person all the time.

- Try to understand what reminiscence means to you and to each individual at the life stage each has reached.

- Identify different responses and styles of reminiscing in other people and think about your own reminiscing style.

- Develop curiosity about your own and other people's past. Do not just see yourself and them through 'present spectacles'. Try to locate them and yourself within an overall life-span that stretches from birth to the present and projects into the future.

- Be sensitive to people who need to forget rather than to remember. Respect their wish to live in the present and do not expect them to reminisce.

Application exercise

1 Now that you have read this chapter, think of three older people you know who enjoy reminiscing. Write down why you think reminiscence is important to each person and why reminiscence is important to you.

2 Could you draw a timeline for yourself, marking in the major events so far in your life?

3 Do you know enough about the life history of the three people you identified to enable you to draw a timeline of their lives?

4 Discuss your work with a trusted colleague.

Further reading

Bender M, Baukham P and Norris A. (1998) *The Therapeutic Purposes of Reminiscence.* London: Sage

Craig C. (2005) *Meaningful Making: A practice guide for occupational therapy staff.* Stirling: Dementia Services Development Centre

Hendricks J (Ed). (1995) *The Meaning of Reminiscence and Life Review.* New York: Baywood Publishingï

Webster JD and McCall ME. (1999) 'Reminiscence functions across adulthood: a replication and extension', *Journal of Adult Development* **6:** 73–85

4 How to begin reminiscence work – the planning phase

Learning outcomes

After studying this chapter you should be able to:

- understand about phases or stages of reminiscence work with individuals, couples and small groups
- identify the responsibilities of senior staff in facilities where reminiscence work is to be undertaken
- be aware of the overall responsibilities of reminiscence workers
- appreciate the importance of the preparation or planning phase
- summarise the reminiscence worker's tasks related to the planning phase

Phases or stages of reminiscence work with individuals, couples and groups

All planned reminiscence work, whether it is undertaken with an individual, a couple, a family, a small group or a larger community group, moves through different phases or stages over all from beginning to end. This idea of structure, although borrowed from groupwork writing, applies to all planned time-limited reminiscence work, regardless of the number of people involved. Writers use different words to describe these phases but all agree that it is important to understand that workers and participants behave differently at each stage and that roles and responsibilities also change at each stage. Within each single session or meeting it is also helpful to use the same idea of structure to check what is happening to workers or leaders as well as to the other people involved.

Shulman (1999) suggested:

- preliminary, preparation and planning
- beginnings
- middles
- endings

Tuckman (1965) suggested:

- forming
- storming
- norming
- performing

Tuckman described 'forming' as the stage of getting together, becoming acquainted, making trial and error suggestions, and much indecision. 'Storming' is the stage when rules and boundaries are tested, anger is expressed and conflict recognised. The group then emerges into the 'norming' stage where agreement is reached about how members will work together, and finally 'performing' sees tasks accomplished. A further stage of disbanding is sometimes added.

This handbook uses Shulman's classification of preliminary, beginning, middle and ending stages. The success of any reminiscence work, including a reminiscence group, largely depends on how carefully the leader(s) plans and prepares for it. Although careful preparation for each session is important, the early and late sessions are the most important. The beginning and ending of each separate session is also important because these are times of heightened emotions and hence important opportunities for work.

Models of groupwork

Just as people have different styles of reminiscing, so groups differ depending on their objectives, leaders' ideas about groupwork and members' characteristics. There are many different kinds of groups, models of groupwork and styles of leadership. Distinctions between models are not always as clear cut as some writers suggest. One appropriate model for reminiscence groupwork is described as a 'mutual aid' group. This means a group where members are encouraged to join in shared discussion as equals on freely agreed topics. It assumes that members have sufficient common experience to feel secure enough to be open with each other. If a person feels their past experience is vastly different – perhaps, for example, because of poverty, education, ethnicity, prejudice or suffering – they may feel very exposed and vulnerable in such a group. It may take them a considerable time to develop trust and confidence and to feel able to participate freely.

Some reminiscence work, whether with individuals, couples or small groups, is better described as an 'activity' or as 'task-centred'. Here the emphasis is on 'doing', on producing a tangible, visible outcome. The reminiscence is important in itself but in this type of group it is a means to an end. This approach concentrates on achieving an agreed outcome or a specific product.

Most local and oral history work devoted to recording, writing and publishing people's memories fits this category. Its objectives may be quite specific such as preserving recollections by sound or video recording, writing a family history, or publishing a record of a local neighbourhood during an identified period. Some people may wish to become historical informants and pass on their historical knowledge to families, school children and researchers. Some groups will want to achieve a single event such as an exhibition, a reading of their written work, a play or performance based on members' recollections to which others are invited. Some may wish to establish a database or an archive. Reminiscence becomes part of the means or the vehicle for achieving these possible outcomes.

Reminiscence work with an individual, couple or group may have a single major emphasis, but seldom are other aspects totally excluded. Many reminiscence groups in care settings, for example, begin as mutual aid or 'talk' groups but, during their lifetime, members may decide to write down, record, publish, illustrate, perform or exhibit the outcomes of their discussions. In such groups both the process and the product are important. In other groups which initially set out to be task-centred, members usually gain other intangible benefits such as warmth, acceptance, friendship, and improved self-esteem and personal growth as their life experience comes to be heard and appreciated by others and incorporated into a tangible outcome.

Reminiscence, once begun, develops a dynamic of its own. If a show, book, exhibition or other product is produced, it in turn will stimulate further reminiscence by the audience, reader or viewer, so the process once begun will have many different and frequently unforeseen outcomes.

Reminiscence therapy

Some reminiscence work, undertaken by professionally qualified therapists or counsellors in which recall of the past plays a large part, is described as 'therapy' or 'psychotherapy'. Groups led by trained psychotherapists are called psychotherapeutic groups. This approach aims to help members uncover complex, painful, perhaps long-buried, traumatic memories and unresolved conflicts that 'leak' into the present and interfere with present functioning, adjustment and well-being. This book does not attempt to equip people for such highly skilled work, which requires professional training and close supervision. Whatever the objectives and emphasis within reminiscence work, if it is a positive, nurturing, constructive experience, freely entered into, for participants it will indeed be 'therapeutic'.

The responsibilities of senior staff

If you are a manager in a hospital, care home, housing with care facility, day centre, library, museum or community arts organisation you are in a key position. You have a responsibility to ensure that the needs of people served by your organisation, particularly older people, for acceptance, warmth, respect, social and intellectual stimulation, companionship and fulfilling activities are sensitively met.

You are responsible for creating a climate in which people feel valued and their life experience validated. You set the lead and other staff will follow. Reminiscence work will happen, and be done well, or will not happen, or be done badly, depending on the lead you as a manager give, the commitment you make and the resources you make available.

Find other staff members who share your concerns, so that together you can create an active participative environment where each person is recognised as a unique individual with a long and interesting life history. Reminiscence work will flourish only if senior managers affirm its importance, staff are allowed time in which to do it (including time for preparation, debriefing and supervision) and feel that they and the work they do is valued.

In reminiscence work, continuity of leadership that enables the development of trust is important. As a manager you must make sure that, if staff are committed to an agreed number of reminiscence sessions, their duty rotas and workload management enable them to be available at the agreed times. If the arrangements for reminiscence sessions are casually altered, participants will feel the work undertaken and the memories recounted are also regarded as of little consequence. As far as possible, you also need to ensure that participants are free from competing or conflicting demands which may make it hard for them to attend at regular times.

Some staff, regardless of responsibilities and seniority, may not be convinced about the importance of reminiscence work. As McKee and his colleagues (2003) reported 'just chatting' is not highly valued, especially in care homes, although the residents regard it as enormously important. Staff may be sceptical about the value of taking time to reminisce and critical of colleagues for wanting to spend time on something they regard as a 'soft option' or not 'real work'. This important point is further developed in Chapter 10 in relation to people with dementia. Do not let reminiscence work be undermined by such attitudes. Care staff will quickly take their lead from managers. If they see that senior staff value reminiscence and enable it to happen, they will be less likely to contribute to its sabotage.

All staff members need to understand the importance of reminiscing and be equipped to respond to spontaneous reminiscence in sensitive ways. Those who wish to develop reminiscence skills should be encouraged to do so by being trained and involved in more formal, planned reminiscence work. Everyone in a facility, however, can contribute in one way or another. All can be involved, for example, in responding to spontaneous reminiscence, assisting in locating materials, lending objects, making suggestions and sharing in celebrating outcomes.

Consciousness-raising sessions about reminiscence work for all staff – administrative, care, domestic, management and maintenance – are a good idea (Gibson 2004). This is one way of identifying interested individuals who could then be offered basic training and progress to leading reminiscence work. If you as a manager are introducing reminiscence work for the first time, it is helpful to discuss it at a staff meeting. Explain to the whole staff the basic ideas underlying reminiscence work. Tell them how you hope the group members and possibly their families may benefit and openly discuss the implications for staff and how everyone can contribute.

If high standards of reminiscence work are to be achieved, supervision of workers will be essential. Either take responsibility for supervision yourself or ensure that alternative arrangements are in place. Chapter 15 contains more information about various ways of providing supervision and support and about the potential of reminiscence work as a staff development tool.

Practical details and issues of confidentiality will also require detailed discussion with the staff group. You need to agree what information arising from the reminiscence work will be shared, with whom and in what format. Who will have access to it? For example, what will be included in care plans? Who will be responsible for writing these and who will be entitled to read them? How will you involve participants in this record-keeping process?

The responsibilities of reminiscence workers

Chapter 3 summarised the different reasons for encouraging reminiscence. Thinking about the people you are hoping to work with, you may wish to concentrate on only some of these aspects. Depending on your experience and interests, you may also wish to read about reminiscence with people with disabilities before deciding whom you want to reminisce with and for what purposes. Chapters 10, 11, 12, 13 and 14 give information about people with special needs, impairments or disabilities. In this chapter general principles are outlined. These will need to be modified when working with people with particular impairments. Be realistic and selective about what you want to achieve. Remember that all the objectives so far identified are not equally relevant to everyone in a particular reminiscence project or group, and they may alter during the lifetime of a group both for individual members and for the group as a whole.

Preliminary, preparation or planning phase of work

Meticulous planning and preparation will largely determine whether or not the work you attempt is effective. Before starting any reminiscence project or group, consider the questions listed below. It is not sensible to give standard answers to these questions but general guidelines will assist you to find your own answers. Your own preparations will depend upon the desired objectives, the characteristics of participants, the context in which the work is to take place and the resources available. Planning must include developing preliminary ideas about the people involved, the purpose of the reminiscence work, the place where it will occur, the programme, the process and any possible product. These considerations apply to preparations regardless of whether you are hoping to work with one person or a number of people. You may think the list of questions that follows is far too detailed, but it is designed to assist new reminiscence workers and to provide a checklist for more experienced practitioners.

The people involved

- Whom do I wish to involve in reminiscence work and why?
- Who is likely to benefit from reminiscence and what will best achieve my objectives in my place of work?
- Do I want to work with one person, a couple or a small group, and why?

Guidance

You will never be able to work with everyone who may wish to be involved. Choices will have to be made. Individual work is suitable for people who are likely to benefit from undivided personal attention or have marked communication difficulties caused by speech, sensory or cognitive impairments. Generally, reminiscence is unlikely to be helpful to people who have experienced serious problems coping in the past and whose present circumstances limit their opportunities for learning new coping skills. Exclude from groupwork people who are excessively private or socially isolated by personal preference, introverted, seriously depressed, habitually tearful, suspicious, hyperactive, obsessional, markedly agitated or aggressive. Some people with such problems may, however, respond to individual work.

Reminiscence with couples provides opportunities to sustain and strengthen mutually supportive, well-established relationships. It provides opportunities for encouraging conversation, providing speech practice (perhaps following a stroke), valuing shared good times in the past when the present is threatened because of physical or cognitive impairment, and creates opportunities for preserving and transmitting family history.

Reminiscence groups provide social and intellectual stimulation, companionship, mutual support and validation. They can diffuse apprehension associated with more intense one-to-one relationships. They appeal to sociable extroverts, to people wishing to develop new relationships and to those who wish to contribute memories of personal experience to public records and accounts of collective history.

Identifying possible outcomes

- What do I hope will be achieved for participants and for myself?
- How am I going to explain reminiscence work to potential participants and what will I call it?

Guidance

It is important to set objectives regardless of the number of people involved. You can set either objectives that look forward in anticipation to what you hope will be achieved or outcomes that look back to what you expect will have been accomplished.

Try to set outcomes in very specific straightforward terms. Your initial statement will probably need to be refined or modified as you discuss it with colleagues and with potential participants. Basically you need to be sufficiently clear about what you want to achieve to be able to say something about possible outcomes. The words you use to name or describe the group should reflect the objectives and its hoped-for outcomes.

Application exercises

1 Write down three statements beginning:

At the end of this reminiscence project/group I would like it to have achieved:

(a)

(b)

(c)

2 An alternative approach would be to write down:

At the end of this reminiscence project/group I would like the participants to have achieved:

(a)

(b)

(c)

3 Writing competency statements about what you expect you will have learned to do is also common:

At the end of this reminiscence project/group I shall be able to:

(a)

(b)

(c)

4 Write a simple explanation of the purpose of the project/group which you could use to invite potential participant(s). For example:

'I would like to invite you to join a small reminiscence group with six to eight members. We will meet for a couple of hours a week for eight weeks. This will be an opportunity for people to share recollections about the past with each other so that you can value your past experience and find things in common with each other.'

'I would like to invite you to join a reminiscence group which will ...' (complete the sentence(s)).

Leadership and staffing

Reminiscing with only one person or a couple requires only one worker. Any more is likely to be overwhelming. Groups, however, raise a number of questions:

- Who is to lead the group? In this book the terms 'group leader', 'reminiscence worker', 'facilitator' and 'enabler' are used interchangeably. There are several related questions:
- Is there to be one leader or co-leaders?
- What preparation time will the leader(s) have?
- Will the leader(s) have any supervision?
- If so, who will provide it and in what circumstances?

Guidance

The number of roles and complex responsibilities in a group justify having more than one leader, especially if the worker is inexperienced. If you are working in a residential facility or care organisation, decide if the leaders are to be managers or direct care staff or a combination of both. Often a staff member paired with a volunteer brings a welcome blend of familiarity and novelty, of security and new horizons. Whoever it is, try to make sure that the leaders are likely to be able to work amicably together. Chapter 8 gives more information on co-working or co-leadership.

If you are working single-handed with an individual or a couple, it is still essential to have adequate time for preparation and opportunities for supervision or discussion of your work with a knowledgeable person.

If leaders or co-leaders are not staff members but are coming into a facility to do reminiscence work, they will need to negotiate entrée. They must take time to learn about the organisation and to meet relevant staff and potential participants. It is essential that managers, care staff and visiting reminiscence workers agree what work is to be undertaken, with whom and under what conditions. Everyone concerned needs to understand their respective roles and responsibilities. Inexperienced visiting sessional workers who fail to clarify expectations and requirements at the outset too often find themselves struggling with groups that are too large or which consist of too many people with complex needs.

Co-working is demanding. It requires sensitivity and effort to develop a trusting relationship founded on mutual confidence and respect. For leaders to compete with each other is disastrous. Roles and responsibilities need to be clearly assigned and may be rotated session by session so that each person develops a range of skills. Take time outside the actual reminiscence sessions to plan and to review each session. Do not say this is an unnecessary luxury and there is no time. Preparation and review or debriefing are essential for successful co-working.

Evaluation of the whole project/group once the sessions are completed is also important but is seldom easy to achieve. Sometimes an independent person who has not been involved in facilitating the work undertakes the task of evaluation. Evaluation means trying to reach a judgement about the value of the project/group, considering as far as possible both the tangible and the intangible costs and benefits involved and for whom. (See Chapter 15 on evaluation.)

In addition to debriefing, workers find that a good way to develop their skills is to discuss their work with someone who is not directly involved in it. This gives an opportunity to look very critically at what happened, how you felt, how you reacted and what you might do differently next time. Such stock-taking is not just for trouble-shooting but also for building confidence and developing skills. Usually this supervisor will be a line manager but it could be someone from outside the workplace who is experienced in reminiscence work.

Membership

• Will the group have open or closed membership?

Guidance

The answer to this question will influence the objectives set, the style of working and possibly the outcomes achieved. Groups with closed membership are easier to lead than open groups and sometimes you may not have a choice because of your work context. An open group accepts members at any time throughout its existence and is likely to have a fluid membership. The group continues even if the membership changes over time. In open groups members join and leave at any time. This means that some members are always at the beginning stage. The development of group identity, trust and cohesion is continually being set back. Longer-standing members may be frustrated and new members may feel like interlopers. In these circumstances relationships do not have the same opportunity to develop.

The setting often dictates whether a group will be open or closed. Groups in acute hospitals, assessment units or respite care facilities, for example, where most people remain for only a short time have to be open. A common experience where everyone is facing the same uncertainties associated with crisis or transition may compensate to some extent for the difficulties associated with open membership. Groups where some members leave and others remain for the duration of the group are particularly difficult to lead although they do encourage natural leaders from among the established membership to emerge.

A closed group has a fixed number of members who join in the beginning stage and remain for the agreed duration of the group. Illness, death or other circumstances may mean that some people are intermittently absent or leave but in a closed group new members do not replace them. A closed group of older people should therefore recruit sufficient members at the beginning to ensure its viability even if some members are lost during its lifetime.

Closed groups move more easily than open groups through the stages from tentative beginnings to established middles to anticipated endings. If handled skilfully by the leaders, these groups give the members a personally valued, satisfying experience of shared work, acceptance, intimacy, respect, development over time and a sense of achievement.

Group size

• How big should the group be?

Guidance

People's ideas about the desirable size of a reminiscence group are very varied. The answer to this question will partly depend upon the competence, confidence and experience of the group leader or leaders. Groups doing simple reminiscence work are probably best limited to eight to twelve members. More experienced leaders may be able to manage larger groups but these should not be confused with large-scale nostalgic recreational activities. Participating in these large events is a different experience from the planned small groupwork advocated here.

Specific reminiscence work is best done with far fewer people – most frequently with individuals. Chapter 10 suggests that reminiscence with people with dementia requires very small groups, usually with no more than two to four members, and individual work is often more productive than groupwork. Chapter 11 discusses reminiscence with people who are depressed and the special modifications required. People with hearing, sight or speech problems find it very difficult to participate actively in groups unless special arrangements such as those described in Chapter 12 are possible.

Forming a group and inviting potential participants

* Who should decide who is to be invited?

Guidance

Actually getting a group together requires careful thought and detailed action, and various people may wish to influence its formation. Whenever possible, questions about who is to be invited to join a reminiscence group in a group care context should be discussed in staff meetings so that consensus can be achieved. In determining membership it is sometimes helpful to use already existing natural groupings. A key worker, for example, might run a group for the residents for whom she has special responsibility. Try to identify other groupings such as people who once lived in the same neighbourhood, worked in the same occupation, came from the same locality, followed the same sporting interests or shared a common experience such as immigration, bereavement, illness or disability. Select people who are likely to feel comfortable with each other and who will enjoy each other's company, rather than made to feel vulnerable, isolated or embarrassed.

Group membership is often talked about in terms of homogeneity or heterogeneity, meaning all the members sharing the same predominant characteristics or, alternatively, having different characteristics. An example of homogeneity might be a group where all members are white

British-born and of heterogeneity being a group whose members are all from various ethnic backgrounds and countries of origin. Even then, of course, this is an over-simplification because, in both these examples, members may have had very different experiences in terms of poverty, education, income and employment. In constituting a group, you need to consider the people you wish to involve and the objectives desired or the purposes you hope that the group will serve.

Sometimes the staff may wish to use a group to integrate people, for example a newcomer or an isolated, solitary person. A reminiscence group may then be used to encourage informal mixing in the hope that it will help new relationships to develop. Sometimes the people who reside in one wing of a facility may form a natural group although the very opposite may work well, as the following example shows.

> **Care assistant** *'In my Home the men and women always sat in different rooms. They seldom mixed with each other. We agreed to hold the reminiscence group in the women's lounge and Mr Smith said at the end of the first meeting how much he had enjoyed visiting another part of the Home. He said it was better than having an outing!'*

Issuing the invitations

- Who should do the inviting?

Guidance

Do not automatically assume that you are the best person to do this. It is usually best if the group leaders issue the invitations but sometimes a key worker or a member of staff who has a special relationship with a person might be better placed to do so. Whoever it is, they must extend a genuine free choice about participation. There are powerful hierarchies in residential establishments and organisations. If powerful staff extend the invitation, some people may feel obliged to accept. Residents may perceive what might look like freedom to staff as coercion.

The format of the invitations

- How are people to be invited?

Guidance

There is no one best way of either selecting or inviting group members. There are many different ways to do both. What is important is to be willing to choose the way most likely to achieve a positive response. Wherever you work, the guiding principle must be open discussion. Sometimes a public invitation on a notice board or a widely distributed flyer works well and avoids accusations of favouritism. Depending on the response, you may then need to think in terms of size and mix of members. If you use this public approach and have more people respond than is manageable, make sure that there will be opportunities to join another group in the future which people will be able to take up.

Staff members tend to think they know best who is suitable and unsuitable for reminiscence work. Sometimes they deny opportunities to people, especially those who are different, demanding or have special needs. Keep an open mind rather than reach hasty decisions. Give people an opportunity to decide for themselves.

Initially, people may not understand what a reminiscence or memories group means. Some people will be reluctant to try anything that sounds new or strange. These same people may soon want to join, once word has got around that the group is interesting – a resident who first refused an invitation later announced, as she 'squatted' in the reminiscence room, 'I know what you are doing in here and I'm coming!'

If you are an inexperienced groupworker, it is unwise to overload a group with too many people with special disabilities.

For your first group, try to select some natural storytellers who will help the discussion along. If the group goes well, your confidence will quickly grow, and in your next group you will be able to risk including people with more complex needs.

Preliminary interviews

- Is it desirable and advisable to meet potential members individually beforehand?

Guidance

Experience suggests that preparatory interviews are usually important although some workers think they are too time-consuming and an unnecessary luxury. Each person should be seen before the first meeting if possible. You can then explain further about the group, gather some details and inquire what themes or topics the person would like to discuss. This interview should be a two-way process. It should give the potential member an opportunity to ask questions to help in deciding whether or not to participate. It should also enable the reminiscence worker to gauge or assess the suitability of the person for the group you intend to form and what topics are likely to interest them.

A Personal History form is given in Appendix 1 to assist you to collect and organise preliminary biographical information. You will need to explain its use, mindful that some people are wary of disclosing personal information to people they do not know well. In some cultures it is thought to be very inappropriate to talk about personal and family matters to relative strangers.

People are usually ambivalent, if not fearful, about committing themselves to a new experience, so you need to use this personal interview as a bridge into the group. Be clear about the invitation, sensitive to any reservations or anxieties, and show genuine respect for the person's hopes and expectations for the group.

This initial meeting contributes to the 'contract' or 'working agreement' you will make with the whole group, so you need to be able to explain the group in simple, straightforward language. Understanding about the objectives or expected outcomes will grow and develop as the group develops. This preliminary meeting, however, is very important in securing initial consent and in making the potential member feel that joining the group is a risk worth taking.

Staff members sometimes think that, because they see the potential members every day as they go about their ordinary work, they do not need to take the time to gather initial background information. This is a mistake. Remember that the success of any project/group is closely linked to the attention given to its planning and preparation.

If working with an individual or couple, it is also essential to explain your intentions, tentatively agree objectives and be explicit about the number, frequency and duration of intended meetings. Be sure to check for feedback from the person or couple involved to clarify any misunderstandings or to identify underlying reservations.

The lifetime of the group

- Will the group be time-limited or open-ended?
- If time-limited, how many times will it meet?

Guidance

Reaching a decision about the duration of a group depends on balancing resources, availability and expectations. Some groups, especially those who see themselves more as local history groups rather than reminiscence groups, are likely to be open-ended and to continue, probably with changing membership, for as long as people wish. They are more like a club or a class, and some continue for many years.

It is customary for formed reminiscence groups to meet for a set number of sessions, usually six to twelve. Because it takes a group time to develop through the different phases, fewer than six sessions is likely to mean that the group experience will be much more limited and less satisfying. Ten to twelve sessions are desirable but be realistic about what you can hope to sustain.

The frequency of meetings

- How often should the group meet?

Guidance

This depends crucially on the objectives or outcomes desired. Once-a-week meetings are conventional but task-centred groups working on a specific project may wish to meet more frequently. Groups for people with dementia usually meet more often than once a week and benefit from an extended overall time period. It is usually better to stick to the agreed number and frequency of sessions rather than let a time-limited group drift on. Finish as planned and then begin preparation for your next group. Sometimes groups decide to transform themselves in terms of type of membership and the time span over which they intend to operate, but it is better for this transformation to be explicitly recognised by the group at some point and a new contract agreed.

A clear commitment to a set number of individual or couples sessions increases motivation and heightens expectations. It also assists planning and helps the workers to organise their own workload.

Location of meetings

* Where will the individual sessions or group meetings be located?

Guidance

Finding suitable accommodation can present many challenges. Make sure you choose a venue that is consistently available for each meeting. People find changes of venue disconcerting. It needs to be well lit, without glare or shadows, comfortable, warm, furnished informally, welcoming, and free from interruptions, distractions or noise. Try not to intrude on other people's 'space', especially if they are not to be included as group members. Such invasions can create resentment. People displaced from their regular sitting areas and favourite chairs may try to assert their territorial rights by gatecrashing.

By holding the group in an unfamiliar place such as an underused staff room in a residential facility, a feeling of excitement and adventurousness can be generated. Hospital wards, short of small rooms and quiet, private day space, present particular challenges. It is sometimes possible, in spite of obvious distractions, to hold a small group around the bedside of a person who is unable to get up. People with impaired mobility may need help to reach the meeting place and participants who use wheelchairs may require extra assistance.

Length and timing of meetings

- How long will a meeting last?
- What time of day is best for meetings?

Guidance

Meetings vary in length according to the physical and mental fitness of the members. About an hour is usual. Additional time needs to be allowed for gathering together, dispersing and having refreshments. About two hours over all is a rough guide. It obviously takes more time for a group to gather, settle, warm to the work, plan the following session, then to wind down, end the session and disperse than it does for a session with an individual or a couple. Try not to be rushed yourself or to rush others.

Think carefully about the best time of day for holding sessions. This will vary from place to place depending on staff rotas, meal times, other activities, care routines and transport arrangements. Find a time that causes least hassle for everyone involved and stick to it. For people with a disability, extra care may be required to identify an optimum time. The agreed time for the agreed number of sessions should be honoured. In these ways workers demonstrate their commitment to the contract and their respect for the work being undertaken.

Escorting

- Who will help the members gather together and disperse?

Guidance

Be sure you have made a clear plan about responsibility for helping members gather and disperse if they are unable to get themselves to the meeting place. Gathering frail people together can be complicated and time-consuming. A co-leader may undertake this task or share it with other staff. Everyone involved will need to understand the importance of timekeeping. Forgetful members will need to be reminded on the day of the meeting.

Seating

- Who will sit next to whom?
- Where will the leader(s) sit?

Guidance

The job of the leader is to make it possible for everyone to participate, so think carefully about how you arrange the room, including who occupies each chair. Try to use the accommodation in whatever way is most likely to encourage the members to talk to each other, not just to the leaders. Allow extra space for wheelchairs and agree with members where to place their zimmers or other mobility aids.

Think about where members may prefer to sit and which arrangements would be most likely to help them feel secure and encourage participation. People may try to overcome their initial anxiety by sitting next to a friend, spouse, partner or familiar person. As the group develops and confidence grows they may be more prepared to take other seats. It is best to sit anyone with a visual, speech or hearing difficulty, or who needs special help, near a leader. If there is more than one leader, disperse yourselves. Do not sit together to bolster your own confidence; sit where you can see each other so you will be able to make eye contact and also see everyone else. Sitting in a circle or around a table usually works best. Many related activities require a table, which can also provide a sense of security and help people to feel less exposed.

Refreshments

- Will refreshments be part of the meeting? If so, what should be served and who will be responsible for providing it?
- What special arrangements may be required for some members?

Guidance

Refreshments are important to most people, especially those who live alone and who may have few opportunities for socialising. If refreshments are to assist rather than distract, careful planning is required about their suitability, availability, serving arrangements and timing. If served at the beginning, they can help anxious people to relax. If served at the end, they connect people together and may make a meeting very special. Leaders need to be aware of and make provision for special dietary, religious and cultural requirements and preferences without making anyone feel embarrassed or demanding.

Suitable food will be necessary for people who have diabetes or other medical conditions. Religious requirements and cultural and personal preferences will need to be considered. If you are working in a care home or day centre the staff will be used to accommodating the dietary requirements of residents but, if not, you will need to think carefully about what is required. See Henley and Schott (2004) for detailed discussion about food and diets for people from minority ethnic communities.

Henley and Schott advise that many Hindus and Sikhs are vegetarian. Some avoid stimulants, including tea and coffee. Observant Jews and Muslims both avoid all animal products except those derived from animals that have been slaughtered according to religious requirements. Observant Jews do not eat milk and milk products within four hours of eating meat or meat products. Shellfish are unacceptable to observant Jews, who may also want to be sure that the cutlery and crockery they use has been kept solely for either milk dishes or meat dishes.

So if you have people of different religions, it is best to avoid offering shellfish or meat, especially pork or any pork derivatives. Animal fat (which, for example, may be contained in shop-bought cakes and biscuits) should also be avoided and vegetarian brands chosen instead.

Always offer a choice of beverages for everyone. As well as tea or coffee, offer herb teas, fruit juice and water. Have disposable cups and plates available for those who might prefer to use them.

Food and its preparation and consumption carries great symbolic and personal significance. It resonates with people's earlier family experiences. Once-familiar food and ways of preparing and serving it, especially taking personal preferences and life-time experience into account, can be enormously evocative; its availability can greatly enrich and encourage the reminiscence process.

Be clear about who is responsible for bringing and paying for the refreshments and for serving and clearing them away. If meeting within a residential facility, try hard to set up timing arrangements that meet the needs and preferences of participants rather than the routines of the domestic staff. This may sound a simple task but its achievement can require considerable perseverance and negotiation.

> **Care assistant** *'It was after we had turned off the projector, put down the things we had been passing around and the tea arrived that the real chat began. I have never seen the group so animated and excited. I do think it was the refreshments that helped to relax them and encouraged them to talk – even Mrs Upta was joining in.'*

Programme

- What themes or topics will the group discuss?
- How will these themes be organised or arranged?

Guidance

The choice of themes or topics for discussion must rest in the hands of the group members. The leader may propose topics but should defer to the group because, in this democratic style of groupwork, the group belongs to the members, not the leader. The leader helps the group turn its ideas into a logical and consistent programme that will achieve the agreed objectives. By reading, watching films or videos or visiting museums, group leaders can familiarise themselves with the broad historical period through which the group members have lived. Through such preparation they will be better able to encourage and understand the recalled memories of participants. Figure 4.1 is a quick-reference age grid that enables you easily to identify how old people were at the time of particular historical occurrences or significant events – for example, during the 1930s depression or when World War II ended – provided that you know approximately when they were born.

Figure 4.1 Quick-reference age grid

Age by												
Born	**1900**	**1910**	**1920**	**1930**	**1940**	**1950**	**1960**	**1970**	**1980**	**1990**	**2000**	**2005**
1900		10	20	30	40	50	60	70	80	90	100	105
1905		5	15	25	35	45	55	65	75	85	95	100
1910			10	20	30	40	50	60	70	80	90	95
1915			5	15	25	35	45	55	65	75	85	90
1920				10	20	30	40	50	60	70	80	85
1925				5	15	25	35	45	55	65	75	80
1930					10	20	30	40	50	60	70	75
1935					5	15	25	35	45	55	65	70
1940						10	20	30	40	50	60	65
1945						5	15	25	35	45	55	60
1950							10	20	30	40	50	55
1955							5	15	25	35	45	50
1960								10	20	30	40	45
1965								5	15	25	35	40
1970									10	20	30	35
1975									5	15	25	30
1980										10	20	25
1985										5	15	20
1990											10	15
1995											5	10
2000												5

Chapter 5 contains examples of some possible themes of interest to people who have spent most of their lives in the United Kingdom. If reminiscing with people from other countries and cultures, be alert to the need to check carefully and modify content and triggers appropriately. Based on the preferences expressed and the information obtained during the preliminary interviews, the worker takes the lead in planning the first session. After that, subsequent sessions need to be planned, at least in broad outline, in discussion with the participants, and part of the ending work of each session is to make plans for the following session. It is always important to follow the interests and life experience of the members. Do not impose your own preferences but do not abdicate responsibility for assisting the group to develop a coherent programme.

There is no limit to the type or range of subjects that can be discussed or related activities undertaken. The programme may be thematic or follow a chronological order, dealing with different historical periods or different life stages. Themes are usually easier for inexperienced workers to manage. Each theme may have within it many different topics, which can be developed over a number of sessions. If you strike a rich vein, with the group's agreement, build on it in future sessions. For example: a session on foreign holidays could be followed by sessions on working abroad, favourite foreign food, money and shopping, exotic clothes, music, souvenirs, films, significant buildings, and friends and acquaintances from other countries.

> **Reminiscence worker** *'I was really interested in the London blitz because my mother had been in it and I wanted the group to talk about that. When I suggested this they said: "No. None of us was in London during the war. Let's talk about weddings – they are nice and cheerful"; and I had to let them.'*

Triggers

- Will I need triggers?

Guidance

Using triggers to encourage reminiscence is a central aspect of most reminiscence work. Triggers need to appeal over time to all the senses of sight, sound, touch, taste and smell because different people respond in different ways. Triggers are especially helpful in the early sessions. Although less common in work with individuals or couples they can also be helpful in shortening the time needed to arouse interest and achieve warm engagement and mutual sharing of experience. Asking a few simple questions often stimulates effective reminiscence. Most experienced workers find that, except perhaps for people with serious cognitive or sensory impairments, triggers are seldom essential but frequently helpful.

Locating and using triggers

- How will I find triggers?

- How will I use them?

Guidance

Try to build up your own small collection of multi-sensory triggers. Collect, beg and borrow objects representing everyday work and domestic life, not grand antiques. Many useful items can be found in junk shops, market stalls, car boot sales and in the attics or cupboards of older relatives. For a small outlay it is easy to pick up second-hand books and magazines, old kitchen gadgets, tools, tins, boxes, cards, coins, clothes, fabrics and household articles. Friends and staff are usually very willing to lend things once they understand their potential usefulness.

Music and other sounds are especially good for evoking memories. Recordings of once-familiar sounds such as the whistle from a steam train, children playing, a school bell ringing or the clip-clop of a dray horse can arouse instant recollections. Smells can stimulate memories, particularly those associated with food and home-baking. For more information about using music in reminiscence work, see Chapter 10.

Many people enjoy seeing pictures or 35mm projected slides, videos, CDs or DVDs. Stories, poems, old newspapers, books, comics and magazines read aloud are very effective. Handling and examining objects, noting their colours, shapes and textures, debating their uses, quite apart from the associated recollections they evoke, can be very enjoyable. Live triggers such as a baby, small child or pet animal can immediately generate interest, even in the most passive, withdrawn people.

Use the natural environment and the seasons of the year. Plants, twigs, bark, leaves, grass, pine cones, fruit, vegetables, nuts, seeds and flowers can all be used. Other examples of multi-sensory triggers are given in Chapter 5.

Libraries, local museums, local historical societies, community groups, churches, mosques, temples, synagogues, local newspapers and photographic archives are all potential resources. Triggers are readily available once you begin to look around and see the possibilities in things you have long taken for granted.

Many trigger packages containing tapes, slides and photographs can be bought. These off-the-shelf trigger materials are useful if you are very busy and have little time for preparation. Without doubt, they have helped to make reminiscence work popular. On the other hand, if you rely on them too much or use them in a mechanical, routine way, reminiscence work will degenerate into nothing more than nostalgic entertainment or just something you feel obliged to do. It is much better to start with people, not triggers. Discover their interests and concerns and then look for triggers that closely match. Always begin with the people, not with the triggers.

Equipment

- What equipment will I require?
- How will I use it?

Guidance

Special equipment is not essential but there are times when some can be very useful provided that you feel comfortable with it. If you plan to use audio recorders, film/slide projectors, video, computers and CDs or DVDs, be sure you know how to work them. You will need to match appropriately the group size and the type of equipment used. You will soon grow in confidence and master the technology, but if you are inexperienced, do practise beforehand. If co-working, take turns to be responsible for this aspect of a group session, as this develops skills.

If you intend to show 35mm slides in daylight, most projectors require reduced light so curtains will be necessary. An extension lead, a table or stand of the required height and either a blank wall, preferably white, or a screen will also be needed. Pre-loading projectors are preferable. The room will need to be darkened but not blacked out completely. Retain some light if possible and sit people in a semi-circle. Be sure that everyone can see the screen, but bear in mind that low light reduces the possibility of lip reading and the hum of machinery adds to people's hearing problems.

So, once the group has had a good look at a picture, you may want to switch the projector off for a time. In any case, slides can be damaged if they are exposed to the heat of a projector for too long. Portable 35mm slide presenters that incorporate a tape recorder are useful but expensive. They project either a small picture about the size of a small TV screen (front projection) or else a large picture suitable for a screen or wall (back projection). They are very useful for taking to a person's bedside or to somebody's own home. Slide presenters can also be used for making your own synchronised tape/slide programmes if you want to put together your own local trigger materials. Computers, including laptops, CDs and PowerPoint data projectors, are now replacing much of this earlier equipment.

A camera, especially a digital one, can greatly enhance reminiscence work. It can be used for photographing possible triggers, places of past significance, group sessions and celebrating work undertaken. Photography can stimulate 'then and now' discussions and a camera is invaluable for producing material for displays and exhibitions. It is also a great asset in individual life review and life story work.

An audio tape recorder for playing and recording sounds, music and recollections is a useful piece of equipment. They vary greatly in type, price and ease of use. Cassette recorders are simple to use but are being increasingly replaced by digital recorders. There is a lot to learn about making good sound recordings but there is no need to be intimidated. Get advice, do some reading and then make a start. (Chapter 6 is also relevant.) Recordings of group members' recollections can be used as triggers in future sessions. In this way each group becomes a potential resource for future work. Camcorders offer enhanced possibilities but bear in mind that poor-quality amateur film has limited use unless it has compensating personal associations.

More people, including older people, are now familiar users of multi-media CD-ROMs, DVDs, email and the Internet. These technologies have great potential to stimulate reminiscence, locate personally relevant triggers, stimulate recall and link people in new and exciting ways. Before buying any audio/visual or computer equipment, seek independent advice from someone who is technically knowledgeable but who does not have a vested interest in selling a particular brand or product.

Make friends with the staff at your local public library. They can assist in innumerable ways. Many local libraries and sound archives lend recorders, projectors, cassettes, CDs, DVDs, videos and pictures, as well as printed material. Increasingly, many public libraries are providing free access to the Internet.

Confidentiality and record-keeping

- Are the sessions to be kept confidential?
- Is there to be any feedback and, if so, to whom?
- What records will be kept?
- Who will write them?
- Who will have access to them?
- What will happen to them when the project/group is finished?

Guidance

As part of preparation, leaders will need to have thought about confidentiality and record-keeping so that in the first session ground rules can be discussed and agreed. This is a part of the contract. The arrangements will vary from project to project and group to group, but it is important that they are always openly agreed and understood. Where reminiscence activity is being used for assisting assessment and care planning, this must be explained.

To be strictly bound by total confidentiality may defeat the purpose of reminiscence groups that mostly generate contagious enthusiasm and infectious pleasure. You and the members may want the mutual enjoyment and group satisfaction to be widely communicated. Sometimes, however, when a group member has disclosed a very intimate or private recollection, the leader may need to contract with the group about treating that particular episode as confidential.

You may say, for example: 'Mrs G has just trusted us with a very private memory. I suggest we all agree to regard it as confidential and not tell anyone outside the group what we have just been told. What do you think? Is that agreed by us all?'

Leaders need to be open about their participation in supervision or consultation. Do not assume that participants understand that staff members may be accountable to line managers for their work. Explain briefly what the arrangements are and what obligations you have to colleagues, managers or funders. Assure participants that discussion and analysis of work undertaken is a necessary part of your professional development and accountability.

Record forms

- Will I need to use special forms?

Guidance

Whether you are obliged to keep records for supervision or not, it is still an excellent idea to do so because it helps you reflect on the work you are doing, week by week, and assists with final evaluation. Examples of various record forms are given in Appendix 1.

Agree who is to write any records and who will have access to them. Be alert to people's sensitivity about literacy skills and adjust demands accordingly. Records should be kept in a safe place. At the very least, keep an attendance record and follow up any absentees week by week. A good way of improving your inter-personal skills is to make a 'process' record of any parts of a group session that went either very well or very badly. Try to remember exactly and write down accurately what triggered these 'critical incidents', who said what, the emotions expressed or withheld, and how you and other people responded. When a project/ group is terminated, decide what is to be done with the records.

Property rights

- Who 'owns' any tangible group outcomes or products?
- What agreed uses might such products have?
- Who benefits financially from any publications or sales arising from the group's work?

Guidance

It may seem strange to be wondering about 'property rights' and sales before your group has even met. This is, however, an ethical issue you need to think carefully about. If you hope that the group might publish, exhibit or in some way make a record of its members' recollections, the group will need to agree and to give permission. If life stories, photos, video recordings or personal memorabilia are to be used outside the group, it is a wise precaution to ask members to sign a simple release form at an appropriate time (see Appendix 1 for an example). People are seldom reluctant to publish but you must not take agreement for granted. Written permission is strongly recommended.

Some people find it hard to believe that their lives are worth putting into print or that their experience could possibly interest anyone else. Even a modest document produced with a personal computer and photocopier can give its author enormous pleasure, pride and satisfaction. Work that is accessible to other people may have implications for people who were not involved in its creation or even know of its existence. Great care needs to be taken about any possibility of misrepresentation or defamation, and you will do well to consult with senior staff and managers to ensure that the requirements of sponsors, host organisations and funders are respected in terms of confidentiality and other ethical issues.

Conclusion

This chapter stresses the need for careful, systematic, detailed preparation. The major decisions required at the planning stage have been identified and guidance given. Use the chapter as a check for planning each new project or group and make brief notes about what you need to do before beginning the first session. Try not to think that because you have led a previous group you can skimp the preparations for a new one!

KEY POINTS

- Take time over detailed preparation. It will pay off in the long run.

- Select members with great care, usually after a preliminary interview.

- The group belongs to the members, not to you. You are an enabler, not an owner.

- Do not avoid problems, hoping they will go away. They won't. They will go underground instead, waiting to sabotage you when least expected. So deal with them openly.

- Learn to begin with people. Build a collection of multi-sensory triggers around their interests.

- Develop the habit of keeping records of your work to help you develop the different skills required at different phases throughout the life of a reminiscence project or group.

Application exercise

Plan a reminiscence project or group, using the checklist to help guide you through the preparation and planning phase.

Further reading

Gibson F. (2000) *The Reminiscence Trainer's Pack.* London: Age Concern Books

Rainbow A. (2003) *The Reminiscence Skills Training Handbook.* Bicester: Speechmark

Shulman L. (1999) *The Skills of Helping Individuals, Groups, Families and Communities.* Itasca, IL: FE Peacock Publishers

5 How to lead a reminiscence group – the beginning, middle and ending phases

Learning outcomes

After studying this chapter you should be able to:

- identify roles, responsibilities and behaviour of workers and members during the beginning, middle and ending phases of a reminiscence group with closed membership
- explain the possibilities and pitfalls associated with using multi-sensory triggers
- differentiate between the major characteristics of reminiscence in groups with open or closed membership
- list examples of universal or common topics or themes

Beginning phase of a group with closed membership

Although this chapter refers to groupwork, much of the content is also relevant to reminiscing with individuals and couples, about which more detail is given in the next chapter. Having completed the planning and preparation phase to the best of your ability, you are now ready for the group to meet. The first meeting of a new group needs to affirm everyone's best hopes, not confirm their worst fears. 'Tune in' to how you are feeling and try to imagine how the members may be feeling as the first meeting gets under way.

Members will probably be feeling much the same as you, both fearful and expectant. They will be ambivalent, torn in two directions at the same time. They will be worried about embarking on a new experience. This is especially so if they have not previously belonged to a formed group, do not know other participants or had previously unhappy experiences in groups. They will wonder what will be expected of them: will they be able to cope?; will they be pressured into talking when they would prefer to remain silent?; will they be overshadowed, or perhaps overwhelmed, by dominating, talkative people?; will they talk too much themselves or give too much away?

While being fearful, they will be looking forward to a new experience, meeting new people, hearing about new things, and wanting to share some of their own past experience and to have it valued and validated by others. If there is more than one leader or helper, tasks should be allocated beforehand so that uncertainties or confusion between leaders does not aggravate the ambivalence and tentativeness of members. Ideally, you will have met the members beforehand but this is not always possible. In order to overcome initial anxiety, be present when people begin to arrive so that you can greet each person by their preferred name, and possibly shaking hands. This may be unacceptably intrusive for some people, so use whatever form of greeting makes each person feel welcomed and reassured. The leader has a crucial role to play in helping people to feel that the effort they have made to come is appreciated and that they will find the experience worthwhile.

Introductions

At the beginning most people worry about fitting in, of having enough in common not to feel isolated – this may be a major difficulty for people who feel different from other members. Depending on whether or not members already know each other, the leader needs to make introductions. Initial awkwardness can be reduced if informal refreshments are available as people arrive. When it is time to begin, the leader should encourage people to sit according to a prearranged but not rigidly enforced seating plan. Some groups begin by inviting people to introduce themselves. This sometimes works well because it involves everyone equally, but it can be very daunting for a shy person to have to speak up right at the beginning of a new group.

Use each person's preferred name – never a name that the leader assumes a right to use. People should be asked what they prefer to be called at the initial interview and their wishes respected. In making introductions, do nothing that might show up anyone's poor memory, or embarrass them in any way. Using nametags clearly printed in large letters greatly assists introductions.

Contracting

Follow the introductions with a brief statement about why you are all meeting together and what you hope the group will accomplish. This introduction repeats the initial explanation you made and the tentative contract you agreed when you first met members. If you did not have the chance to meet people beforehand, the introductions must be very clear and you need to 'reach for feedback' to make sure the members understand and agree about the purpose or objectives of the group.

A simple opening statement from the leader might be: 'We have agreed to meet here today and for X weeks at Z time to talk about past times and to share our recollections with each other. Usually people find it enjoyable and helpful to talk about our memories of the past, and today we shall begin by talking about Y. Later in today's session we shall make plans for the other meetings. Is that all right with you all? Do you have any questions?'

Leaders need to clarify what it is hoped the group can offer its members and what the group might accomplish. This 'contracting' work is very important because it makes the members feel that the group genuinely belongs to them. It also means that in future meetings, if anyone wants to use the group for some other purpose – for example, planning a fundraising event or pressuring a local politician – you can return to this agreement or contract. It can then be reviewed and participants can democratically decide if it still represents their wishes, or in what ways it should be changed.

New leaders find it very hard to 'reach for feedback' at the beginning of a new group. This is because you will be anxious that the arrangements you have worked hard to put in place at the planning stage might be upset and your plans undermined. Do not be afraid of trusting the group. A group has to be mutually satisfying to be successful. It never will be if you insist on imposing your own agenda. Encouraging everyone to talk who wishes to express an opinion and then, after discussion, asking

'Does everyone agree that we shall do ...?' or 'Is everyone happy with these plans?' or 'Does someone have another idea?' indicate a genuine desire for the group to be founded on mutuality, with everyone sharing and participating as equals.

Ground rules

Some leaders like to agree ground rules at the beginning to try to help a group discipline itself but, if this is done too early or too insensitively, it may make the leader look more like a bossy teacher rather than an enabler or facilitator. This misperception may happen anyway if the leader is already familiar as an authority figure – perhaps as a senior member of staff who is already known as the 'boss'. All groups actually start long before the first meeting to which people bring their prior experience and personal preconceptions, so what may seem like a democratic group to you may not be seen in quite the same way by all the members.

A leader might say: 'Do you think it might be helpful if we agreed a few simple rules among ourselves so that everyone gets a chance to join in?' Seek feedback. 'Is that all right?' Then continue: 'I don't want to sound like a referee but it may help if we agree that everyone who wants to talk should get a chance to do so. Could we agree that only one person speaks at a time, so everyone can hear? Is that okay? I suggest that we should respect different points of view, and not use unkind, hurtful or offensive language. We need to accept that old memories might bring up strong feelings. We might get a bit emotional at times. No one needs to feel embarrassed if this happens. We also need to talk about confidentiality. Maybe we should take these points one at a time ... What do you think? ... Are these suggestions okay?'

It is a mistake to use the first session exclusively for contracting and planning. Although some time must be spent on these aspects, be sure to do some reminiscing so that members leave with a feeling of excitement and a first-hand flavour of what they have come together to do. Otherwise they will be disappointed and puzzled. An opportunity for the group to grow together through shared work will have been lost.

Sessional structure

Every session has a beginning, middle and end that should guide the leader's behaviour. So, when the introductions and the preliminaries have been completed, introduce the first topic or the first trigger by asking a simple question such as 'What does this remind you of?' or 'What does this take you back to?' or 'What comes to mind when you think about ...?' Don't rush. Follow the pace and mood of the group. Do not worry if the discussion seems untidy or disjointed. It usually takes two or three sessions for a group to settle down, for everyone to feel comfortably relaxed and sufficiently confident to initiate discussion or to listen patiently to other people. Keep observing the members continuously so that you are aware of their responses. Be finely tuned to the emotions being expressed, not just the words. Reach out to anyone who looks uncomfortable or upset, and value everyone's contribution.

Timing

Watch the time. Stick to the agreed arrangements because, if you do not, others will probably be inconvenienced. As the time gets close for ending the session the leader should begin ending work by reminding the members that time is nearly over for today, briefly summarise what has been done and suggest that the group makes plans for its next meeting. Every small detail about all future sessions does not need to be agreed but the broad directions do.

For example, the leader may say: 'Time is nearly up for today but we still have X meetings ahead. You remember that we agreed that we might possibly talk about A, B or C. What order do you think we should take these in? What would you like to cover in the next meeting?' After an agreement has been reached, check it out. Ask: 'Is that all right? Are you all happy with this suggestion?' When the necessary arrangements have been agreed, indicate that today's meeting is over and that you will be looking forward to next week. People who need to leave can then do so even if others want to linger a while.

Reminiscence groups often start again after you think a session has ended! Do not be worried about this. Animated conversation may also continue outside the session and it may involve others. This does not matter provided that agreements about confidentiality are honoured. Holding a reminiscence group prior to lunch in a day centre, for example, usually results in members energetically continuing to reminisce over lunch; members' enthusiasm is the very best advertisement and is highly infectious.

Group process

Each subsequent session should begin with a modified form of group contracting, sometimes called sessional contracting, and end by spending time planning the next meeting. Every group is dynamic – it grows and develops over time, so you will need to help it to be responsibly flexible. Agreements or contracts are not straitjackets that should never be modified. On the other hand, a group needs coherence and order if it is not to be a free for all, at the mercy of the member with the loudest voice.

Many inexperienced leaders worry about 'losing control'. They imagine that somehow the group will run away from them, people will either talk too much or talk too little and that good order depends on the leaders. Such worries are diminished if you realise that you are a part of the group and that, although you have special responsibilities, the group belongs to everyone in it, not to the leaders.

People behave differently at different stages. Do be patient. In the beginning phase, most members (and leaders) are anxious. Some people will talk a great deal and appear to be very domineering. This is often a cover for insecurity. Others will retreat into silence and yet resent the seemingly confident talkative members, even though such dominance saves the quieter person from feeling compelled to talk.

In the beginning, members tend to talk more to the leader than to each other. Friends and acquaintances may talk to each other and to people sitting next to them but they may seem to ignore, or not be interested in, what other members have to say. People may lack the confidence to talk to the whole group but they relax in time and there are ways of helping everyone feel more comfortable. Spending some time in a paired activity and then sharing this work with the whole group can help build confidence in early meetings. Seating arrangements, themes, topics and related activities and how the worker behaves also impede or assist the growth of confidence and mutual trust.

Using triggers in the early sessions can bolster an inexperienced leader's confidence. Triggers, if carefully chosen, quickly arouse interest and encourage conversation. Triggers used in the beginning stage of a group should relate generally to the known life experience of as many of the group members as possible and not be restricted to a single member. At this early stage avoid triggers that are likely to relate to potentially intimate, painful or private experience. Topics and triggers should not trap people into too early or too intimate disclosure.

If you want to encourage a silent or shy group member to participate, you can purposely select triggers that relate very closely to their background and which they quickly recognise and feel knowledgeable about. In this way you may very gently lead them into talking and sharing. Give people time to develop trust in each other before you expect them to share recollections of painful, contentious or very personal experiences. This will come once the group has developed trust or intimacy in the middle phase of work.

Middle phase of a group

After two or three meetings, the group moves into the middle phase. It begins to feel less tentative, surer of what it is doing, safer and more cohesive. During this stage, trust, respect and courtesy gradually emerge. People attend to what others are saying and respect divergent points of view. The talkative, dominating member gradually learns to listen and the quiet, retiring member, feeling valued, begins to talk.

Sometimes there may be a few members who cause unease in the group. Monopolisers feel compelled to hold forth and to prevent others from speaking. They may have been welcomed at the beginning but increasingly they will irritate other members who are likely to show their disapproval by non-verbal behaviour. Some people remain aloof or isolated from other members although they may very much wish to be fully accepted. Feeling rejected by others, they may become increasingly hostile, which increases their isolation still further. Some people act the clown, seek attention or compete with other members or with the leader who is responsible for helping each member to feel comfortable, trusted, secure and valued within the group.

A scapegoat is a member on whom the hostility of the group is projected. Others may recognise in this person the characteristics they like least in themselves. The scapegoat may be an innocent victim but is more likely to have characteristics that provoke the other members to treat them badly. The leader must actively encourage full participation of all members from the beginning by providing direction and guidance. If such dysfunctional roles still become established, the leader must be able to engage the group and the particular person in discussion about what is happening. By the middle stage, members are more able to examine and discuss such problems openly and suggest solutions. The worker must not take sides but be able to see all sides and to help each member feel able to contribute constructively to the group.

Asking questions

Even the type of questions a leader asks can encourage or discourage discussion. Learn the difference between open-ended and closed questions. The first invites descriptions and elaboration of events, experiences, situations and feelings. The person answering the question decides what to say or not say. The choice is theirs. Closed questions tend to feel like a cross-examination. Save such questions for filling in later details once the discussion is flowing freely. For example, 'Tell me about your school days?' is an easier starting point than 'What was the name of your first teacher?' And 'What do you remember about starting work?' is better than 'What kind of clothes did you wear on your first day at work?' Most closed questions require only the briefest answers. Some have only right or wrong answers. So if a person lacks confidence or is unable to remember on demand, rather than risk getting the answer wrong, they will probably prefer to say nothing.

Open questions, on the other hand, like those below, leave control of what is told in the hands of the storyteller and invite responses that others can add to, embroider and develop.

- Please tell us about your childhood?
- What sort of food did you like as a child?

- What sort of games did you play?
- Tell us about your wedding, please?
- What is your happiest memory?

There comes a time when it is appropriate to look for more detail, to encourage people to explore their memories in greater depth and to re-encounter, reconstruct and reappraise their memories. During the beginning phase, leaders and members need to tread softly while each develops the confidence that comes from working together and earns the privilege of hearing and sharing the more intimate, emotionally laden memories that emerge during the middle phase of work.

Leaders need to learn to be aware simultaneously of the group as a group and also of all the individual members. This may seem a tall order but the skills of observation and empathetic response grow with practice (Doel and Sawdon 1999). Having a co-leader greatly assists with keeping track of how each person is responding. You need to communicate with your whole body. Use eye contact, lean towards people to engage them, nod to encourage the silent members to contribute but do not pressure them to do so. One simple trigger, or just a short open-ended question, may be sufficient to start people talking but triggers that stimulate different senses in sequence are powerfully evocative.

As the leader, do not regard yourself as the historical authority. You are an enabler whose task is to encourage the members to talk to each other. They are the authorities and the teachers. If the focus from the outset is on the members' own life experience and personal memories, then obviously they are the experts. Your responsibility is to help them make connections between their own experience and the experience of other members.

Inexperienced leaders often use too many triggers. They seem determined to use everything they have prepared, even if discussion is flowing freely. Try not to be driven by an urge to stick to your own agenda. You have to be orderly and responsive, systematic yet flexible. You need to follow the flow and feelings of the group. Respect the pace, preoccupations and mood of the group as a group and each separate member. Do not rush or pressure people but also be alert to possible boredom, restlessness or resistance. Sometimes your best-laid plans can go astray, as this worker found:

> **Leader** *'Because the slide projector wasn't available we used two large pictures as trigger material. One was of a shop and the other of the inside of a country cottage. Although I was worried about having to change my plans and the amount of time ahead, I was pleasantly surprised to find the group members getting great enjoyment from talking about every detail in these pictures. As Mr K talked I could see a transformation taking place. The members changed from passive observers with very brief comments to excited participants who could not wait to talk about churning, milking and local creameries.'*

Responding to pain and loss

As time goes on, members will begin risking stories that have layers of meaning. They may try out different versions according to how they 'read' or perceive their present audience. Some may feel sufficiently safe to talk about painful recollections. Others may be reluctant to do so, frightened of their own pain – perhaps fearing being left worse off, rather than better off, as a result of allowing a long-buried hurt to resurface.

Leaders need to be particularly alert to loss in all its many guises. No one grows old without experiencing repeated loss. This may be of loved ones, family, friends, relations, home, neighbourhood, belongings and pets. There may also be diminished energy, ill-health, removal from special places and lack of once-absorbing interests. As loss emerges and people face the inevitable comparisons between their past and present circumstances, resistance to further exploration is unavoidable and responding sensitively to such reluctance becomes part of the leader's work. Some members may want to talk whilst others may be afraid to listen because they fear being overwhelmed by the pain aroused in themselves by hearing other people's recollections.

Many leaders find it hard to encourage members of reminiscence groups to share pain. In a million ways they damp it down, choke it off and encourage the group to retreat into superficial conversation. Learn to overcome your own reluctance to share another's hurt. Point the group members towards each other and make links between the members' experience. In uncovering memories they discover common ground and become rich resources for each other. If you are a young leader, older group members will probably know more about loss than you do, so use their vulnerability, their resilience and their strength to help the whole group.

Emotion will never be far from the surface in any reminiscence group. Quickly the mood can change from gaiety to sadness, from laughter to tears. Do not be afraid of tears nor think you have done harm if people cry. Inevitably some people will recall very painful past experiences. This recall may bring distress but also relief, in that it may be the first time such memories have been shared with others. Too often we try to protect ourselves from pain by fleeing from other people's tears, sadness, disappointment or anger.

Learn to respect silences. Do not be embarrassed nor hurry people on. People need time if they are getting in touch with deeply felt emotions and they need time to organise their thoughts and decide how much they will tell. It is not a time for rush or bustle or hollow responses. Most of us dread silence. Learn to wait out the silence, then to name the expressed emotion and then to link the experience and the emotion of the individual with the experience and feelings of the rest of the group members. The group is the resource. Use it to the full, but be aware that follow-up outside the group may also be necessary. Very occasionally a person may need expert professional help to resolve recurring memories of past trauma. It will be your responsibility, in consultation with others, to ensure that the person is referred with consent for counselling, psychotherapy or other professional assistance (Hunt, Marshall and Rowlings 1997).

A few members may never talk or they may talk very little but their body language will indicate how they feel about the group. Silence does not necessarily mean lack of satisfaction. Try to understand what the experience means for each individual and enable them to use the group in whichever way best meets personal needs.

When members begin to contribute their own personal triggers, this is a sure sign that the group has become important to them. Great sensitivity is needed, however, as some members may no longer have access to cherished possessions. A thoroughly satisfying experience for some members may heighten a sense of loss or isolation for others. Seeing other members contributing personal memorabilia may increase their own feelings of loss and separation or dislocation from their past lives unless facilitators encourage them to talk about objects of personal significance even if they are no longer physically accessible to them. Suggest to these people that they recall for the group a significant object and describe it and its significance.

Loss of momentum

During the lifetime of a group, energy and involvement will fluctuate from meeting to meeting. Over time, if members seem to lose interest, do not just silently deplore this, feel hurt or blame yourself. Try to understand what is happening and openly address the issue. Confronting is a very necessary skill in groupwork but it is one that leaders are often reluctant to use, especially in groups for older people. Confrontation means facing people with the implications of their behaviour that may be preventing the group from accomplishing its agreed goals. Confrontation must be accompanied by genuine empathy – otherwise group members will experience the leader as hostile. Confrontation does not mean blame or combat. It means honestly exploring difficulties, facing up to problems, having open discussion and jointly agreeing how to proceed.

Absenteeism

If the group is a formed group with closed membership and a member is absent, this should be acknowledged in the session. Any absences should be followed up by telephone or visits and explained to other members. Sometimes people change their minds about participating, deciding that reminiscence is not for them. Such views should always be respected but make sure that there is no other hidden reason for a person withdrawing which requires remedial action by the leader.

In groups with a predominantly aged membership, intermittent attendance, serious illness, hospitalisation and deaths are not unexpected. Such events must be openly acknowledged and this will demonstrate to other members that, if they experience similar problems, they can expect to be treated with equal respect and care. In residential facilities careful communication with staff members will be essential if regular attendance is to be maintained. Other demands and institutional routines such as bathing, medical treatments, chiropody, hair appointments and unscheduled visitors can so readily intrude and assume greater importance.

Ending phase of a group

In time-limited groups that meet for an agreed number of sessions, it is usual to foreshadow the end of the group from the beginning. Each week members can be reminded of how many sessions remain. In these ways the end is anticipated from the outset. Endings, like beginnings, are a time of increased opportunity for work because they are a time when feelings are more exposed. Groups that have been successful, that have worked well together and shared much, end with less pain than those that have never really 'got going'.

Even in successful groups, however, members will experience mixed emotions around the ending phase because they will be separating from the leader and from each other. Some may feel relieved that the group is over. Others may resent that it is not continuing, or feel sad or angry that they must face another 'ending'. Leaders may feel pleased with their achievements or possibly guilty because they did not accomplish more. Probably everyone involved will experience a mixture of these varied emotions.

In the ending phase, leaders have a big responsibility to make sure that the ending, with its mixed emotions, is openly addressed. Do not let your group just fade away, even if some members have anticipated its ending by ceasing to attend. Unfinished business needs to be addressed, achievements reviewed and work evaluated. Use part of the last session for stock-taking. Invite the members to look back, to acknowledge the work they have done together and to say what the experience has meant for them.

Try not to be talked into extending the life of the group. You may be placed under considerable pressure to do so – 'just a few more sessions'. Stick to the contract but be open about how people, leaders included, feel because the group is ending. Resist trying to deal with your own feelings by promising something in the future that you cannot deliver. If there is a realistic chance that there can be another reminiscence group, say so. Do not make promises you cannot keep. Common examples of unrealistic promises include saying you will continue to visit a facility or will visit people in their own homes. Facing the pain of separation openly is more constructive in the long run than pain denied.

Many groups try to handle their strong feelings around endings by giving themselves a farewell party, which tends to emphasise the positives and ignore the pain of impending termination. Of course, there is a place for parties, special events and celebrations but if these are left until the final session, rich opportunities may be lost for building on a positive experience, which is often better situated before the final group session. A shared outing or other special event at that stage could be relished, recalled and used subsequently as a basis for further work. The final meeting can still be special if it reviews, evaluates and celebrates the work accomplished.

If the group has agreed to produce a tangible product such as a publication or exhibition, make sure you deliver on this. Be clear about the time-scale and mutual responsibilities. On no account promise a product that you do not have resources to produce.

> **Roger Sim, a Hospital Arts worker,** believes: 'It is important in any arts or reminiscence project to mark achievement with a celebration or ceremony – both to thank and acknowledge all those who have been involved and also to attract the attention of managers and those who may be in a position to resource future developments.'

Endings also mean that the leaders need to review and evaluate the work undertaken. Just as after each session it is important to spend time considering how the session went, so at the end you need to look back to reflect on all the work you and the group have done together. Review your notes from each session. Review what you said you hoped to achieve and what has been accomplished. Try to be realistic, do give yourself, co-leaders and members credit for work accomplished as well as facing up to the things that could have been done differently, or done better. It is good to achieve success and to understand why a project or group has been successful so that next time you undertake reminiscence work you will be able to replicate effective practice and improve upon it. (See also Chapter 15.)

Open groups

In reminiscence groups with open membership, meaning that membership changes from meeting to meeting, group intimacy may never be achieved although individuals may still find the experience constructive. Each meeting will need to be self-contained because continuity of participants and programme will not be guaranteed. These groups tend to rely more on triggers and set programmes, less on spontaneous exchange of personal experience, and require the leaders to provide more active direction. Such groups usually aim to provide recreational activities and social and intellectual stimulation; often they are considerably larger than formed groups with closed membership.

As the length of hospital stays decreases, and respite care and short-term admissions increase, formed groups with closed membership become more difficult to sustain, except in long-term care facilities and community settings. Do not assume that groups in hospitals and care homes will work in the same way as groups in day centres. You need to be alert to each distinctive context of care, its particular constraints and opportunities, and be willing to modify or adapt your reminiscence objectives, programmes and practice to meet the needs of different people and the characteristics of diverse working environments. Because it may not be possible to gather initial background information from individuals before they participate in an open reminiscence group, the programme should cover topics of universal interest that are likely to appeal to all participants. A skilled facilitator will still be able to achieve involvement and discussion between participants but the group is unlikely to display the same degree of purposeful engagement, trust and intimacy as a closed group.

Using multi-sensory triggers

Many different approaches can be used to stimulate the sharing of memories and to encourage people from various cultural backgrounds and people with disabilities to participate. There are triggers that possibly have universal significance whereas many others are likely to be culturally specific. Do not assume that what is meaningful to you will necessarily be relevant to everyone else. Both verbal and non-verbal communication is important in reminiscence work. Some groups may like to draw or paint, sometimes accompanied by music, to read, write or recite poems, to sing, dance, act, tell stories, complete proverbs, do quizzes, make collages, mosaics or wallhangings, and draw maps or family trees. Many of these activities are also appropriate for working with individuals and couples. Some activities may also be viewed as end-products or tangible outcomes of reminiscence work. (A list of such products is given in Chapter 6.) There is no limit to the possibilities, provided that people freely agree, feel supported not pressured, and no individual is made to feel in any way inadequate, demeaned or deficient. It is customary to describe triggers as appealing to the senses of vision, sound, touch, taste and smell. Many triggers simultaneously stimulate more than one of the five senses.

The discussion that follows refers primarily to the general experience of the majority white population of the UK. To appreciate the different experience of immigrants from other countries and cultures who are now growing old in the UK, *Mapping Memories: Reminiscence with ethnic minority elders* edited by Schweitzer (2004) is a valuable source. People from Pakistan, the Caribbean, Africa and the Far East recount their stories in this book and matching CD, and many ideas about culturally sensitive triggers and creative activities are also given.

Visual triggers

Visual triggers are the most readily available and include pictures or paintings of people, places, things and events. Posters, maps, flags, drawings, diagrams, documents and certificates are all possibilities. Photographs are widely used in reminiscence work but it is important to know that people from some religions and cultures are wary of photographs and some forbid them altogether. Some strict Moslems, for example, forbid images of both people and animals, so photographs depicting either are unacceptable.

There are three broad types of photographs: personal, artistic and documentary. Look for photographs that combine the personal and the documentary. Even if you want to use a picture of a particular place, one that portrays people and if possible action will be a more effective trigger than a beautiful lifeless scene. Use pictures of ordinary people doing ordinary things. Photographs are powerful memory joggers and they also reveal much about people's backgrounds but people may not always be ready or willing to talk about them. In all effective reminiscence work, respect for people, regardless of age, culture, ethnicity, gender, income, politics, religion and sexual orientation, is essential. Discriminatory attitudes, conversation and behaviour are unacceptable. Leaders need to model sensitive anti-discriminatory practice at all times and to be willing and confident to address any form of discrimination if it surfaces in a reminiscence group.

A professional picture of a great public occasion may not be nearly as effective as personal snapshots of reasonable quality. Pictures of public events – for example, the coronation, the assassination of President Kennedy or Princess Diana's funeral – can be used for asking people 'What were you doing on the day when ...?' This approach links the public event and its personal impact. Such events vary enormously in their impact on individuals and may be of little interest or relevance to some people either from Britain or from other parts of the world. Take care also if using such an approach not to choose events that may make some group members feel defensive, uncomfortable or isolated.

You may be fortunate in locating a local public photographic collection or a private collection belonging to someone who has documented community changes over the years. Local photographers are often delighted to discover a 'therapeutic' use for their life-long hobby and willingly lend or copy their pictures.

There are many large public photographic collections in various parts of the UK. Some of these public collections require appointments to view, or sometimes photocopies can be mailed to help you decide exactly what you want before ordering copies – which may be very expensive and take several weeks to obtain.

The digitising of photographic collections now means that a large number of images can be placed on a CD-ROM or DVD, and a search facility makes it easy to locate specific pictures or groups of pictures concerned with specific topics or subjects. A laptop computer, screen and data projector enable easy viewing of enlarged pictures. The Northern Ireland Film and Television Commission's digital film archive (see Appendix 2) is one such invaluable collection that is being used extensively in reminiscence groups, including inter-generational groups.

Enlarging and mounting on laminated board increases a photograph's usefulness and prolongs its life. Several copies of the same picture enable group members to examine them closely and discuss them with each other. This is a useful technique if people have hearing, sight or speech difficulties.

Newspaper articles and advertisements may be photocopied and enlarged. Again, getting them laminated, mounted or put in plastic covers will extend their life. Plastic covers unfortunately reduce the impact of most pictures. Colour photocopying produces high-quality copies cheaply and quickly. Computer technology, digitised archives and digital cameras have transformed the ways in which trigger materials can be located, accessed and shared. Modern technology, including the Internet, now makes it much easier to obtain visual and auditory triggers that match or closely relate to the known life experience of individual people and communities.

Objects too precious to handle may be photographed. Postcards, books, magazines and newspapers are another source. Local newspapers frequently publish photographs of past times with accompanying articles that are excellent for reading aloud. A reminiscence session may need little more than a local newspaper or an old advertisement to start discussion. Appendix 2 lists some commercial publishers and distributors of reminiscence materials. Help the Aged's (1981) three *Recall* tape/slide programmes with notes are still widely used and may be available from libraries. Several other packages modelled on *Recall* are available for different parts of the UK and Ireland.

Slides, audiotapes, CDs, DVDs, videos and films need to be used very selectively. They can result in passive rather than active viewing if you let yourself become the captive of technology. Any reminiscence aids or triggers must be regarded as servants, not masters. Their purpose is to enable people to talk actively with each other, not just to sit passively watching or listening to yet another 'show'.

Historical films should be used cautiously. A few minutes' viewing may be sufficient to stimulate discussion. Many programmes made for schools are useful for reminiscence groups of all ages. Video recorders are fast becoming obsolete as film libraries and others switch to CDs and DVDs.

Auditory triggers

Memory for sounds can be vivid and immediate. Usually a sound is associated in the mind's eye with a visual memory and it may be quite impossible to separate the two. By triggering one, both are evoked. Sounds, especially music, provided people do not have impaired hearing, can be very evocative. Collections of recorded sounds – for example, of animals, trains, cars, bikes, sea, wind and rain, appliances or machinery – are readily available. There is also music of all kinds and periods, film soundtracks, stories, poetry, proverbs, plays, lists of place names, auto-biographies, documentaries and local dialects. You may also want to make your own recordings. Local radio is a rich resource, as the closer the sounds, speech and accents match people's own background, the richer will be the response.

Music

Music is particularly effective because it immediately arouses emotion. It stimulates attention while also usually being relaxing, making people feel at ease. It can be enjoyed in its own right and also for the associated memories it triggers. Locate music that reflects varied tastes and experiences. Get people to tell you what music they once enjoyed, now prefer and would like to hear again.

Live musical performances are very popular. Identify talent within your own workplace or neighbourhood. Many older people have retained musical abilities that can be revived and give pleasure to themselves and other people. 'Procedural' memories, including the ability to play musical instruments, are well retained. People require encouragement and opportunity to perform but many can still do so. Provide opportunities for older people to acquire new musical skills. Most people can play simple percussion instruments with little instruction. Encourage active participation in music making, including singing rhymes, hymns and songs. But beware of making older people feel patronised. There is a world of difference between recalling or re-enacting childhood experience and being treated as a child. Recorded music, karaoke tapes, song sheets and large-print songbooks are useful.

If using group singing, give all members a chance to suggest a song, even if they are not keen to join in the singing. Respect everyone's choice and make sure that no one feels embarrassed. Home would have been the focus for entertainment for older people. Singing around the piano and listening to the radio or phonograph would only slowly have been replaced by television from the 1950s onwards. (Chapter 10 contains more information about linking music and reminiscence work.)

Tactile triggers

Handling objects provides instant pleasure and encourages immediate recall. Just holding something, looking at it, feeling its weight, shape and texture, then passing it to the next person links people together and stimulates cumulative shared memories. Objects encourage demonstration of how they were used – another example of drawing on long-term procedural memory. Objects invite activity, shared opinion and animated conversation. Avoid using objects that can only be admired from a distance. Everyday items such as working tools and household gadgets that people can handle and pass to each other without fear of damage are preferable. Strange objects whose function is not immediately apparent encourage debate, even disagreement, and lively discussion.

> **Day care worker** 'We had a dolly, which is a thing used for washing blankets, but hardly anyone knew what it was for. Someone said it was an ear trumpet. Another person said it was for clearing drains. There were the greatest arguments. Everyone joined in and enjoyed the fun.'

If you select triggers with care, over the weeks everyone's life experience can be represented in one way or another, and this encourages everyone to feel that their past, and consequently themselves, has been acknowledged and their stories heard.

Tastes and smells as triggers

Even if these senses diminish with age, tastes and smells can still be used, either alone or combined in sequence with other triggers, to enrich a theme or explore a topic. It is very easy and inexpensive to make your own smell collection. Put the same substance or liquid into several matching small bottles or containers that can be passed around a group; a lively guessing game spontaneously erupts.

Similar and contrasting smells encourage people to identify, distinguish and name the smells as well as to discuss the contexts in which they were used and the associated memories that they evoke. Some possible smells include:

- disinfectants and household products – carbolic soap, Jeyes fluid or mothballs
- toiletries – baby powder, lavender water or eau de cologne and cosmetics
- medicines – menthol, castor oil, petroleum jelly (Vaseline) and boric acid
- herbs and spices – rosemary, mint, chives, nutmeg, cinnamon and ginger
- flowers, vegetables and other plants – lavender, eucalyptus, sweet pea, cabbage, leeks, garlic, turnips, carrots and potatoes

Old-fashioned sweets and drinks such as liquorice, jelly babies, 'conversation lozenges', sherbet and ginger beer can still be purchased and used to stimulate recall. Reminiscing about favourite food, associated smells, shopping excursions and related people and events can be easily encouraged. Reading stories aloud, looking at old recipe books, recalling food produced for special occasions, packets, tins, wrappings and advertisements can all be used. Vivid recollections are achieved by actually preparing, serving and eating special food. Cooking old favourites can also involve other staff members in the reminiscence work. If it is possible, involve all members in some aspect of the food preparation, advice, instruction, recalling associated memories and eating the outcomes.

Reminiscence on the theme of food may be a way of reviving rusty cooking skills and rekindling or creating fresh interest in nutrition and personal care, and may be especially useful if people are beginning to pay less attention to these aspects of daily life.

> **Care worker** *'We were talking in one session about summertime, gardening and fruit picking. This led on to what our mothers used to do with the fruit and we began to talk about making jam. Mrs Smith said how she wished she could still make plum jam and the group then decided they would like to do that, with everyone sharing a part of the job. We got a lot of help from the kitchen staff but everyone did something to help. We all had such fun. The best part was when everyone had scones for tea and ate our group's plum jam. We were so pleased with ourselves.'*

A cooperative activity like this could be focused on many other cooking or household tasks such as butter-making, cooking pancakes, making soup or baking bread. It could also incorporate a trip to orchards, farms, gardens, farmers' markets or shops. Shared tasks could involve polishing silver and brasses, sanding and painting objects, cleaning and polishing cars or planting out seedlings. Practically all activities can call on past learning and be enriched by swapping stories with other people.

So many reminiscence-linked activities are possible that instead of listing them here, use your imagination to think of ways of enriching spoken or written stories on the themes below through linked activities or actions. This process will stimulate further recall by reviving other memory systems; it bonds people together and provides great hilarity.

Examples of themes

- childhood
- school days
- home life
- clothing
- housework

- work
- wartime
- leisure
- travel

Any of these themes could be used for several sessions or just for one, depending on the interests of the group, the triggers available and whether the group might like to write or record its recollections. These stories could then be read aloud and used to link subsequent sessions. Many of the suggested triggers relate to more than one theme. Each broad theme has many different topics within it. Only some of the many possible themes and topics with related multi-sensory triggers are listed to help get you started. These themes and topics may need to be adapted to represent the diverse experience of all the people involved. Let your own imagination get to work. Discover the innumerable possibilities all around you.

Appendix 2 gives information about organisations that hire or lend themed reminiscence boxes. Many local museums and libraries now offer such services as well as Age Exchange and other local reminiscence centres. Loan materials usually have to be collected and returned by the borrower and sometimes a deposit or a borrowing fee is charged.

Topics	Triggers
Childhood	
Parents and grandparents Brothers and sisters Rhymes, songs and riddles Street games and pastimes Toys, dolls, teddies, books and comics What you did on a wet day How you spent Sunday Visiting the sweet shop What work your parents did Taking care of younger children Clothes you used to wear Rewards and punishments Surprises and disappointments Doing odd jobs and messages Pocket money	Conkers, skipping rope, dolls, oil of cloves, brandy balls, aniseed, sherbet fountains, liquorice, mint balls, paradise plums, gobstoppers, barley sugar, jelly babies, chewing gum, Dinky cars, board games, comics, club badges, cigarette cards, clockwork toys, tinplate and plastic toys, hopscotch tawes, teddy bears, marbles, old money

continued over

Topics	Triggers
School days	
Journey to school	Slate and pencil, chalk,
School building, classrooms and	reading book, copy book,
playground	exercise book, crayons, wall
First day at school	chart, maps, jotters, ink,
What I kept in my desk	inkwell, nib, pen, fountain
Teachers – favourite and least favoured	pen, Biro, textbooks, school
Learning to read and write	photographs, school clothes
What I kept in my pencil case	and uniforms, school bag,
Lunch-time and break time	books, badges, school bell,
Playground games and sports	roll call, reciting tables,
Truanting, mitching, bunking off or	reading poems and stories,
missing school	singing, school songs,
Best friends, gangs and secret places	school reports, programmes
My proudest and most embarrassing	from speech days and
days	sports days
Special occasions, speech day, sports	
day	
Leaving school	
School reunions	
Home Life	
The street where I lived	Photographs, maps, carbide
The home or place where I grew up	lamp, torch, safety razor,
Bathing and hair-washing	shaving brush, nutmeg
Meeting people and making friends	and grater, snuff, paraffin
Courtship and marriage – 'In my day	lamp, Jeyes fluid, mothballs,
...', 'Young ones now ...'	carbolic soap, shroud and
Pregnancy and childbirth	bed linen, Vicks, camphor,
Illness, home remedies and cures	cookery books, cards,
Death and funerals	curling tongs, pre-decimal
Christmas and other festivals	money, photograph albums,

Topics	Triggers
Home Life *(continued)*	
Favourite food Recipes and cooking Shops and shopping Friends and neighbours	Christmas decorations, flowers, plants, seed packets, seed catalogues, gardening tools and mail order catalogues
Clothing	
Changing fashions Children's clothes Teenagers' gear and hair styles Working clothes Best clothes Handing down and making do Home dressmaking	Clothing, underwear, corset and stays, apron, braces, hats, gloves, shoes, boots, shoe polish, button hook, scarves, hat pins, lavender, mothballs, cosmetics, perfumes, jewellery, furs, collar stud, tie pin, shoe last, spats, stick-on soles, thread, sewing and knitting patterns, wool and needles
Housework	
Domestic routines Household appliances Wash day Starching and ironing Drying clothes Dyeing clothes and household articles Going to the launderette Mending, darning and sewing Shopping	Wash tub and board, dolly, knob of blue, Sunlight soap, flat iron, gas iron, electric iron, starch, feather duster, clothing, knitting needles, sock needles, darning needle, electrical appliances, sewing machine, cooking utensils, kitchen equipment

continued over

Topics	Triggers
Work	
My first job and how I got it	Pay-packet, lunch tin,
My first pay packet and how I spent it	advertisements, train and
Mates at work	bus tickets, union card, job
Pay and working conditions	advertisements, horseshoe,
Strikes, lockouts and industrial unrest	ears of wheat, corn, barley,
Being unemployed	hops, tools, working clothes,
Travelling to work	typewrier, photographs of
Leaving home, going into digs	mates and works outings
Emigrating to seek work	
Rural work and town work	
Being apprenticed	
Domestic service	
Shop and office work	
Giving up work to raise a family	
Experiencing retirement	
Wartime	
World War I and II	Films and books, pictures,
The day World War II was declared, and ended	paintings, reading war poetry, letters and diaries,
Where I spent the war	evacuation instructions,
How the war impinged on the place where I lived	ARP warden's helmet and arm band, ration book and
Life in the armed forces	coupons, identity card,
Americans and other servicemen	service uniforms, medals,
Women's war work, munitions factories and land army	maps, gas mask, recordings of Gracie Fields, Vera Lynn
Rationing of food, clothing, furniture and petrol	and other wartime music

Topics	Triggers
Wartime *(continued)*	
Air raids and air-raid shelters, fire watching and ARP wardens Evacuation and returning home Keeping the home fires burning – civilian and voluntary work What happened in my family after the war Other wars and conflicts that have involved me or members of my family When my father returned from the war	
Leisure	
Going on day trips and holidays A day at the seaside Cinema, music hall and theatre Dancing and dance bands Games and sporting events Hobbies and pastimes Pet animals and birds Evenings at the pub or club Day at the races, dog track or match Public transport, bicycles, cars and motorbikes Package holidays and foreign travel Works outings	Cinema ticket, chocolate box, ice cream wrapper, concert programmes, postcards, holiday snaps, bathing suits, beer mats, matchboxes, sand, shells, sporting equipment, bus, train or tram tickets, recordings of rock or jazz musicians, souvenirs and holiday brochures or posters

Conclusion

Ambivalence is common during the beginning stage of a group, while trust, intimacy and significant, and sometimes painful, memories emerge in the middle stage – when important work is accomplished. The ending phase requires skilled leadership and celebration of work accomplished and memories shared. Many themes and topics are available for exploration. It is very unlikely that available subjects will ever be exhausted although varied ways and means will be needed to evoke people's memories. Multi-sensory triggers will encourage people to share their life experiences. Make full use of the natural environment, people's own possessions and special but ordinary triggers that appeal to all the senses and relate to people's known life experience.

KEY POINTS

- The beginning and ending phases of a group are times of heightened emotions.

- It is important to learn to listen to people's pain and sadness as well as to their joys, achievements and humdrum everyday experiences.

- As a leader, promise only what you can deliver and make sure you deliver what you promise.

- Triggers that appeal to all the senses in turn encourage shared recollections and lively discussion.

- Start with people, discover what might interest them and then locate relevant triggers.

Application exercises

Undertake these exercises either on your own or with a potential co-leader:

1 Choose a theme or a topic and write a detailed work plan, listing preparations you will need to make and possible available triggers you would like to use. Identify any related activities and possible tangible products or outcomes.

2 Run the group you have planned.

3 After the group is finished, write a short closing statement summing up achievements for the group and for the leader(s).

(a) 'The group achieved ...'

(b) 'I (We) learned to ...'

(c) 'I (We) need to continue to work on ...'

Further reading

Crimmens P. (1997) *Storymaking and Creative Groupwork with Older People.* London: Jessica Kingsley

Haight BK and Gibson F. (2005) *Burnside's Working with Older People: Group process and techniques.* Boston: Jones and Bartlett

Osborn C. (1993) *The Reminiscence Handbook: Ideas for creative activities with older people.* London: Age Exchange

Sim R. (1997) *Social and Creative Activities with Older People in Care.* Bicester: Winslow Press

6 Reminiscence and life review work with individuals and couples

Learning outcomes

After studying this chapter you should be able to:

- understand the difference between spontaneous reminiscence and prompted or planned reminiscence

- undertake simple reminiscence, life story work and structured life review with individuals

- distinguish between guided autobiographical writing and life story book techniques

- appreciate the importance of non-verbal communication

- use various techniques for recording and representing people's memories

- appreciate and explore relevant ethical considerations

Reminiscence work with individuals is often referred to as life story work or as life history. In this chapter the words are used interchangeably unless particular distinctions are made. Spontaneous and prompted reminiscence and various methods or approaches for working with individuals are described. Reminiscence work and oral history also share many common features, which are explained in more detail in Chapter 7. Much of this general chapter is also relevant to reminiscing with people who have various disabilities, such as dementia, depression or impaired hearing, sight or speech, people with learning disabilities and people approaching the end stage of life. Chapters 10, 11, 12, 13 and 14 give further information about the special requirements imposed by these conditions.

Spontaneous reminiscence

From time to time everyone experiences spontaneous, apparently unprompted recall of memories. Whether these memories are 'entertained' privately or shared publicly with other people depends on personality, circumstances, capacity, motivation and opportunity. This recall may be a fleeting experience or time may be spent recalling a whole series of linked memories. Sharing these recollections with another person enriches and extends the recall process. Carers in residential facilities and day centres and in domiciliary care as well as volunteers and family carers need to appreciate the importance of encouraging rather than discouraging such spontaneous reminiscence. Many seen and unseen events prompt such memories – an unexpected sound, a whiff of perfume or after-shave, children in the street, an animal outside the window or a particular taste or tune.

Such unexpected memories surprise us; they take us unawares and leave our past experience exposed. When this happens to someone in your presence, respond with interest, ask an open-ended question that encourages the teller to follow the memory trail exposed and continue the exploration. Try to understand what the memory recalled means to the other person, both its significance in the past at the time it was laid down and what it means now in the present circumstances.

In caring situations there are many opportunities to use such spontaneous reminiscence. You do not always have to be 'sitting comfortably' to reminisce. Often you may be bathing someone, for example, dressing a wound, making a bed, tidying a bedroom, helping a person to dress or to eat. When these unprompted opportunities arise, seize the moment – it may not come again.

Planned reminiscence with individuals

In addition to these casual opportunities, you may decide to do planned or prompted reminiscence work with an individual. This may be undertaken for many of the reasons suggested in Chapters 2 and 3. You need to understand why you wish to work with an individual instead of a group and to be able to explain what you have in mind. As in groupwork, you need to 'contract' with the person so that they understand what is intended.

There should be a genuine choice about participating and the person must know that they can withdraw at any time.

Individual work also needs careful preparation. All the same questions about why, when, where and how need to be considered. Individual work, just as groupwork, may vary in terms of objectives, methods and outcomes, depending on the contract agreed and the skill of the worker. Memory and imagination interact through the process of reminiscence to help us to construct a life story or life script that we can live with. The story locates us within our family and within a wider community and public context. It provides a sense of continuity by helping us to appreciate who we are, where we have come from and where we are going. The life story connects the present and the past and gives perspective to the struggle between hope and pessimism, integrity and despair as older people confront the future (Erikson 1982).

Getting started

Inexperienced workers often worry about the beginning phase of working with an individual. How will I get a shy, reticent person to start reminiscing? Will I be intruding on their privacy? Why would they want to talk to me?

A number of techniques may help. One way to start simple reminiscence might be to suggest that you accompany the person on an imaginary walk down the street where they grew up. Get them to describe what they see, telling you about both the place and its people. They may like to draw a plan or diagram from memory and then name the various buildings. It then becomes very natural to talk in more detail about some of the residents and different events that occurred in the street.

This idea can be developed by asking them to visualise the place in which they lived as a child and begin to walk, in their imagination, through it, telling you what is in each room. People can be asked to imagine the cupboard in which they kept their toys or their clothes, a shelf in their kitchen, garage or greenhouse and then to talk about what was kept there and what the different things were used for. Depending on their interests, they could be asked about friends at school, members of a sports club or team, mates at work or members of their family.

Some people respond to the suggestion that they should imagine their life as if it were a garden, a special place or a party and then to fill in the details from their own personal recollections. Once begun, the memories usually flow.

The relationship you make with any individual person is the important thing. This grows out of purposeful work, a journey taken together. It is based on mutual respect. Warmth, acceptance, concern and genuineness are the ingredients required if people are to entrust you with their life story.

Using triggers with individuals

Many of the suggestions about using triggers with groups can be applied to work with individuals. You need to consider the person, objectives, relevance and appropriateness of what you are planning. Enlarged personal photographs are very useful but do not forget other kinds of triggers, especially things that can be touched and handled. It is helpful if you can discover an individual's preferred sensory pathway; then you can deliberately choose triggers that are more likely to evoke memories. Listen carefully to what people say. Phrases like 'I see that ...' or 'I hear what you are saying' or 'I think ...' will give you useful clues about how people process information and therefore what types of sensory triggers might be most helpful. This pinpointing of a particular pathway is especially useful when encouraging people with sensory disabilities, dementia or depression to reminisce.

Be alert to using a person's own triggers if they are available. This is obviously easier if they are living at home, where they are likely to be surrounded by all kinds of memorabilia. If they are living away from home, you may need to ask relatives and friends to locate triggers. Follow the interests and preoccupations of the person, trying hard to obtain triggers that relate closely to their known life experience.

Making a tangible product

Think carefully about whether you want to contract about making a record or a tangible product. Explain some of the different ways this could be done. Individual work may consist only of talking together. Sometimes it may be very natural to suggest that a permanent record is made of these conversations. Never impose this on a reluctant person. Be sensitive to any tendency for them to devalue their experience, dismissing their life story as being of no interest to anyone else and therefore not worth preserving. Women frequently dismiss the importance of their experience and may need considerable encouragement to start life story work: 'It's not worth writing down', 'I was only a housewife' or 'I never did anything very interesting' are common initial responses. If a permanent record, no matter how modest, is produced, it may be kept only as a private document or be shared with others. Either way it can be of immense value to its owner. If shared, it becomes an effective tool for ongoing communication with potential to become a valued family legacy. Various formats for making and displaying records are described in this chapter.

Life review, reminiscence and autobiographical writing

There are many different ways of doing specific or concentrated work with individuals. Only some are mentioned here but similarities and differences between life review, reminiscence and guided autobiographical writing are described. All these approaches are based on the idea that, by developing a life story, we can make ourselves more interesting to other people and more acceptable to ourselves. The story helps us to accept with patience, humour and hope both other people and ourselves.

Evaluative life review

Life review is the kind of reminiscence that contains a large element of stocktaking or self-evaluation, of coming to terms with life as it has turned out. Although still based on recalling and talking about the past, it is more deliberate, systematic, reflective or considered and it results in seeing or understanding the past in a new way. Butler (1995, page17) stresses this aspect:

> 'Reminiscence has a constructive purpose ... The life review should be recognized as a necessary and healthy process in daily life as well as a useful tool in the mental health care of older people.'

He suggests that people benefit from the opportunity to express their thoughts and feelings to someone willing to listen. This encourages them to reflect upon their lives so as to resolve, reorganise and reintegrate what may be troubling or preoccupying them.

It is generally accepted that interest in 'putting one's life in order' is most intense in old age although many adolescents also struggle with similar issues of identity and self-esteem. A life review can be triggered spontaneously when people of any age are faced with events or crises that confront them with questions about their own identity and the meanings they attach to life. Life-threatening illness, bereavement, broken relationships, bankruptcy, unemployment, moving into care, crises and transitions of many kinds, both public and private, and awareness of growing old and the inevitability of death can precipitate such stocktaking.

Thinking, remembering, daydreaming and writing are all kinds of social interaction with oneself, even if no audience is involved. Having an audience, however, whether as listener, reader or viewer, does seem to help to develop a 'good story'. This means a story that makes sense of life's experience, not necessarily a story with a happy ending but one that represents a person's life in a way that is acceptable to the teller. People may achieve this by working alone – for example, when they write a memoir or an autobiography. It seems to help, however, in producing a coherent story, a personally acceptable account, if there is interaction between the teller and a hearer, so the reminiscence worker fulfilling this role makes a considerable contribution.

Structured life review

Although some writers still use the term 'life review' loosely to refer to aspects of reminiscence that contain an evaluative element, it is increasingly being used in a stricter, more technical sense. Barbara Haight (1998, page 86), a nurse educator and researcher, defined it as:

'A short-term structured reminiscing intervention conducted on a one-to-one basis with an older person. The person who conducts the process acts as a therapeutic listener who guides the older individual in his or her memories, and helps that individual to reframe troubled events and to move on in their thinking.'

Reminiscence, guided autobiographical writing and life review have both common and separate characteristics.

A structured life review:

- is undertaken with individuals, including those with depression, and is used selectively with people with dementia;
- is a planned and purposeful intervention to which the person consents;
- usually relies on verbal questions, not on multi-sensory triggers;
- is evaluative in emphasis – the meanings or interpretations attributed to the events recounted are more important than the events themselves;
- is therapeutic in intention – to help the person come to terms with his or her life;
- is time-limited with a set number of sessions, usually eight weekly, one-hour sessions undertaken in private, but the number and frequency of sessions may be adapted;
- is designed to cover the whole life-span from birth to the present;
- is structured so as to be a chronological or a thematic account;
- is a systematic process, based on a tested research-based format.

The life review worker:

- guides the person to consider questions concerned with death, grief, fear, religion, school, hardships, sex, work and relationships;
- assists the person to analyse troubled events, to achieve their integration and to move on;
- uses reflective counselling skills, and for this limited time the worker becomes a confidante;
- may use Haight's Life Review and Experiencing Form (LREF) to guide the interview (see Gibson 2004, pages 301–306);
- uses measures of depression, life satisfaction, communication and cognition where appropriate before and after the life review, to assess changes over time;

- produces a tangible taped, written, visual record or an illustrated life story book;
- may undertake a parallel but separate review with a spouse or partner.

Distinguishing characteristics of reminiscence and life review

Reminiscence may be undertaken with either individuals or small groups, and can be used with people either with or without dementia. Although planned, reminiscence does not necessarily systematically cover the whole life-span but may explore a particular time, period, event, theme or topic. Reminiscence frequently uses multi-sensory triggers to promote recall. It is not deliberately therapeutic in intention but may turn out to be so. It is not necessarily evaluative or integrative, although aspects of the process may be evaluative because it fulfils various personal, social and cultural functions. Reminiscence may be limited to a fixed number of sessions or be open-ended whilst its content is not usually tightly structured or rigidly systematic. The worker acts as an enabler or facilitator, not as a counsellor, although the worker seeks to be responsive and reactive and will be prepared to explore feelings and meanings to some extent. Frequently, reminiscence will use various creative means to record and present tangible outcomes of the process. Often spouses, partners or other people may share in the reminiscence process.

Guided autobiographical writing

This approach, developed by Birren and his colleagues, blends individual work and groupwork (Birren and Cochran 2001). It involves individuals writing on set topics and then sharing their writing with others in a group. The method combines private recall and reflection with support in a mutual-aid group as a means of promoting self-acceptance, insight, personal development and social opportunities.

In guided autobiographical writing:

- individuals attend ten weekly small-group meetings of about 6–10 members;

- in between sessions, at home, each person prepares a short two-page written account about nine aspects of life;
- group members then read and discuss their writing in the group meeting;
- group members provide feedback, support and confirmation for each other that life has been worthwhile.

This approach has a sound research base and groups are facilitated by leaders with professional expertise. It appeals to people who are socially confident and reasonably educated, and is a particularly fruitful way of forming new relationships at a time in life when other significant relationships may be lost.

The nine aspects covered in order are:

1 history of the major branching points in life or the time and nature of important decisions;

2 family history;

3 career or major lifework;

4 the role of money in life;

5 health and body image;

6 loves and hates;

7 sexual identity, sexual roles and experience;

8 experiences of and ideas about death, dying and other losses;

9 influences, beliefs and values that provide meaning in life.

Selection of participants

Birren and Deutchman (2005) stress the need for careful prior selection of members of autobiographical groups, because it is rarely desirable or advisable to exclude a group member once he or she has joined a group. They advise against including anyone who is likely to:

- dominate the discussion;
- go off on tangents;
- not want to write two pages each week;
- be shy or reticent and slow the discussion;

- make negative or judgemental comments;
- pose as an expert on every topic;
- speak when others are speaking;
- withdraw from the group, looking displeased;
- share very serious material at an early session before the group has developed trust;
- want to behave as a therapist.

Research outcomes from guided autobiographical writing groups

Research studies reported by Birren and Birren (1996) identify the outcomes listed below for individuals participating in these groups. Participants experience:

- a sense of increased personal power and importance;
- recognition of past problem-solving strategies and their application to current needs, problems and anxieties;
- reconciliation with the past and resolution of past resentments and negative feelings;
- resurgence of interest in past activities or hobbies;
- development of friendships with other group members;
- greater sense of meaning in life;
- ability to face the nearing end of life with a feeling that one has contributed to the world.

Other creative expressions of life review

Similar individual, group or mixed approaches that combine verbal reminiscing and non-verbal forms of expression such as painting and drawing to illustrate different aspects of life experience are also growing in popularity. Important elements of life may be represented in innumerable ways. Stories may be illustrated with simple drawings and diagrams. Spontaneous or rehearsed drama, mime, dance and music can involve people of all ages actively re-presenting, reworking, reintegrating and reconstructing aspects of their personal pasts. Many poetry and creative writing groups have a distinctly biographical, retrospective emphasis although the choice of topic is usually left to each group member. Such writing frequently has a life course focus without being as tightly structured or as comprehensive and deliberately evaluative as either individual structured life review or guided autobiographical writing groups. (See also Chapters 13 and 14 on end-of-life issues.)

Using life stories to illuminate present behaviour

Whether working with individuals or small groups, in all caring contexts there will be some people whose behaviour presents challenges to carers and to reminiscence workers. We all communicate through our behaviour. Some people may be excessively demanding and hard to please, noisy, aggressive, hostile, uncooperative and unhappy. Others may be equally challenging because they remain aloof, isolated, negative and seem to be either unwilling or unable to join in the life around them. Remember that all behaviour has a purpose, even if the purpose may be hard to understand. We all communicate as much through our behaviour as our words and even more so when overtaken by dementia and some other disabilities.

The meaning behind problematic behaviour is not always easy to understand and is likely to need some unravelling. Some people may have unrecognised physical pain or discomfort, some may need concentrated personal attention, some may be depressed, grieving, lonely or miserable. Some difficulties may stem from unrecognised and unmet cultural or religious needs. Life-time experience, current circumstances and present needs will all influence present behaviour (Jones and Miesen 2004).

Frequently a detailed knowledge of a person's life story can provide clues to why they are as they are now, and some of this information can be gathered through reminiscence and life review. If you can reduce the person's unhappiness and troubling behaviour by your understanding responses, you will improve the quality of life for this person as well as for everyone around them.

Too often staff members attach labels. They 'give a dog a bad name' and then are surprised that the person behaves in exactly the ways expected. Try to pay particular attention to troubling and troubled people. Observe them closely, spend time with them, learn about their life history and find imaginative ways for them to convey their life story. Consider whether it could be possible that the way that you and other people relate to them is, in some ways, responsible for the difficult behaviour. When words fail, behaviour becomes a substitute and carers must learn to 'read' this non-verbal way of communicating.

The more you know about a person's past, the more likely you are to understand why they are as they are in the present. This means that you must take time to listen, to discover – probably from various sources – about their past and then to use your understanding to reach them in the present (Hubbard et al 2002). Work hard to create situations where the person truly feels 'heard' and respected as a unique individual.

Some people may have been very badly hurt, whether in the distant past or the more recent past. They may be reluctant to talk. It may take time for them to trust you. Some probably never will. A key worker system in care homes makes it more likely for warm, caring, trusting relationships to blossom.

Many attitudes, approaches and routines encourage difficult behaviour because they serve the purposes of the staff or the institution more than the needs of the residents; they are not person-centred. Some routines are so long-established that no one actually knows why certain things are done in certain ways, other than that they always have been!

Try to discover whether behaviour that you find difficult is caused by the myriad ways in which staff convey their disregard, the routines they impose, or whether it springs from past pain or unmet present personal needs, including physical pain or discomfort. A careful assessment will help you decide on possible causes and solutions. Any responses will need to be put into practice on a trial basis, because you may never fully unravel the causes of the behaviour. Both personal and environmental factors that interact with each other may be involved.

Being in care is a sort of bereavement, an awful disturbing loss, and the resulting grief can be very difficult both for the older person and for others around them. Being in care may also revive memories of past loss and grief, emotions that are then re-experienced in the present as fresh abandonment.

A few people tell the same story over and over again. It is very hard not to lose patience with them. This 'obsessive' reminiscence seems to offer little satisfaction to either teller or hearer. It becomes a recitation of negative experience that the person seems able neither to accept nor to forget. Reminiscence is not helpful to such people if they are unable, after a time, to move on from dwelling on such memories. They may respond better to other activities that distract them from their preoccupations or to cognitive behavioural counselling through which they may learn techniques that encourage more positive thinking.

Generally, however, whenever you start listening to older people telling their life stories, you need to be prepared to follow wherever they want to take you. You need to be open to hearing them, reading their non-verbal behaviour, and respecting and responding to both the details of the story and to the associated emotions that the story teller is experiencing in the present.

> **Care assistant** '*It was as well that I was there when Tom started to talk about his time as an air raid warden and how he had not been able to get a child out of a building. I listened very carefully and I then asked him about other times and he was able to tell me how he had helped bring out a whole family in a later raid. I do think it helped him not to get stuck just on what he had not been able to do. I helped him see the other side of things as well, to remember times where he had succeeded, and not to blame himself as much as when he first began.*'

Recording, preserving and representing reminiscence and life story work

There are innumerable ways in which the outcomes of reminiscence with individuals, couples or groups can be represented in tangible formats. Time, commitment, talent and resources will all influence decisions about what to do and how to do it. Producing any tangible reminiscence product will be demanding for all involved. Therefore the production process must promise to be enjoyable, and the desired outcome achievable and satisfying. The desire to leave a tangible record behind motivates many people. For some a product is evidence of keeping faith with those already dead. For some it is satisfying evidence of continuing ability to complete a defined task. It may be a means of attaining increased personal understanding and validation, and a way of raising public awareness of times past and lives lived.

Products vary from simple to complex; some are short-lived, others durable; some are created for personal satisfaction, others for public consumption; some require few financial and human resources, others require a mix of skills and assistance from many people.

Many of the approaches described briefly below provide rich possibilities for involving colleagues, family members and friends as active participants, partners and contributors. The process itself, as much as the outcome, enlivens caring and enriches relationships. Producing a tangible product must always remain less important than the reminiscence relationship and communication on which it is founded. It is well to remember that, although involving family members in reminiscence work can be mutually enjoyable and rewarding, some may discover, perhaps for the first time, aspects of their family history that they find deeply disturbing. This can mean that what and how memories are to be publicly represented involves careful exploration and sensitive negotiation.

Only a small number of products are described below. Table 6.1 lists more possibilities, many of which combine performance, visual and written aspects.

Table 6.1 Tangible representations of group, couples' and individuals' personal memories

Performance	Visual	Written
Audio recording	CD-ROM	Archive
Charades and mime	Collage	Assisted
Cooking	Display	autobiography
Copper working	Drawing, diagram or	Autobiography
Dance	chart	Book
Drama	DVD	Diary
Excursion and outing	Exhibition	Letter
Gardening	Embroidery and	Life story book
Movement	tapestry	Magazine or
Musical composition	Family tree or time	newspaper
Musical show	line	Memoir
Reading aloud	Genogram	Play
Recitation	Installation	Poetry
Singing	Jigsaw	Postcard
Song writing	Life story book	School report
Story telling	Map	Scrapbook
Theatre	Memory box	Spiritual
Trip, visit or	Model	autobiography
pilgrimage	Mosaic	Story
Walking or heritage	Mural	
trail	Multi-media	
Woodwork and	presentation	
modelling	Painting	
	Papier maché	
	Photograph album or	
	display	
	Pottery	
	Quilt	
	Quiz	
	Quotations	
	Rug	
	Sampler	
	Sculpture	
	Stained glass	
	Storyboard	
	Video diary or portrait	
	Wallhanging	

Source: Gibson (2004)

Life story books

The idea of life story books or 'This Is Your Life' type scrapbooks has been adapted from childcare work. Some care homes ask new residents to bring such a record with them at the time of admission in order to help staff begin to make relationships and to aid communication. The book is used to introduce the newcomer and assist settling in. Others make the preparation of a life story book an integral part of a key worker's relationship-building in the early days following admission. Such books also serve as 'passports' if a person needs to be admitted to hospital or transferred to another facility.

Life story books take many forms. There is no standard way of either preparing or presenting them. Some may be very simple, others more elaborate. It is best to compile them in a way that makes it easy for alterations or additions to be made. Some form of loose-leaf binder to which extra sheets and plastic pockets can be added is preferable. Loose-leaf cellophane photograph album sheets can also be used but are less versatile.

It then becomes relatively simple to organise and preserve personal writing, tape transcriptions, photographs, significant personal documents such as school reports, birth, death and marriage certificates, invitations, letters, personal papers, newspaper cuttings and pictures, and other materials about the person and the period and places in which they have lived. Issues of ownership, access, consent and confidentiality are very important and must be negotiated with each person who is asked to work on creating such a record. (See Chapter 13 for additional information.)

A life story book should be thought of as a 'living' or dynamic document, a record in progress, not a completed static product. It is subject to change, modification and expansion as its owner continues to reflect upon their life's journey. The process of preparing it can be as important as the final outcome. It is a record of the past as well as a record for the present. It can be updated from time to time but the story is never fully told. Even after a person dies, he or she lives on in the memories of others, exerting a physically absent yet important present influence.

Photograph albums

Photo albums, with or without explanatory notes, can be a way of constructing a life story book. Usually the photographs are arranged in chronological order over all or chronologically within themes. Some minimal identification and annotation greatly increases the usefulness of the album.

Family trees

These create a sense of continuity by visually locating the person in time. They may also be incorporated within a life story book. There are computer software programs for compiling family trees but they are not hard to draw by hand. They can be photocopied and enlarged for display in people's rooms in residential facilities. Sensitivity is needed when compiling a family tree because people may have unconventional families that they find are complicated to represent or publicly display. Always seek agreement for what is proposed, and do not proceed without it. Life maps and network diagrams are similar diagrammatic representations with brief text added about significant events and people.

Time lines

These focus attention, stimulate recall and help both teller and listener to keep track of what is being told. They are a simple chronologically structured way of recording major milestones and significant life events. Often illustrative photographs are added. It is easy to add to the personal record, if people wish to do so, a parallel time line that shows major national or international events, which helps place the personal history within a public perspective, and vice versa. They are a helpful training tool for nursing and care staff, as the process of preparation requires exploration with the person and usually a family informant, which helps to individualise the person and locate their present behaviour and circumstances within a lifetime perspective.

Memory boxes

Various containers have been used, including shoeboxes and ammunition boxes. Any available receptacle that enables a three-dimensional representation of a person's life to be created can be used. Photographs, documents, personal memorabilia and cherished artefacts are arranged as their owner directs. Such boxes have great potential for involving other family members or younger people in inter-generational projects. A memory box represents an individual's memories, not a group's collective recall, although people often meet in groups with each person being assisted by a worker or volunteer. If constructed in group sessions, there will be some general discussion of how the work should proceed, and there will probably be group reminiscence about universal themes. Each person then creates their own box, assisted by their personal helper whose primary task is to facilitate the recall and only secondarily to assist with the technicalities, not the key decisions of how the memorabilia is arranged in the box. It is customary to exhibit the boxes publicly to celebrate the lives of the people who created them and to stimulate the exchange of further reminiscences.

Boxes are also used as private repositories of memorabilia of personal significance. An example comes from a KwaZulu-Natal project where reminiscence workers are helping families in which parents are dying from HIV/AIDS to record family history tapes and collect memorabilia. This is stored in boxes to serve as legacies for their surviving children (Denis and Makiwane 2003). In this project copies of tapes are archived in the local university to ensure that they survive the ravages of time and the possible death or dispersal of other family members.

Wallhangings, collages, quilts, mosaics and murals

All of these may be either individual or group representations of themes, places, events and people. Usually their preparation runs in parallel with the reminiscing that informs the content, and involves considerable discussion and effort over an extended period of time.

Storyboards

These provide a visual summary of the major events in an individual's life story, gathered by means of reminiscing and consulting other available informants and sources of information. Usually incorporating photographs, they have been used by the bedsides of people in residential and hospital settings and for people admitted for short-term respite care. They also have great potential in home care where a variety of helpers may be calling. Day centres or sheltered workshops may undertake both the initial reminiscing and the creation of the boards or else these are prepared in people's own homes by reminiscence workers or volunteers. Displayed in people's own homes or by their bedsides in a health or social care facility they provide both a tangible reminder of the lived experience and information and a focus for conversation with professional carers, family carers and visitors. Less elaborate scrapbooks or annotated photograph albums can be used in similar ways.

Audio tape recordings

Audio recording remains popular in both group and individual reminiscence work. It is much easier to make a good-quality audio recording of an individual than of a group. Transcribing an audio recording, although a time-consuming task, increases its usefulness. As a learning tool, a tape enables you to analyse and reflect upon your reminiscence skills and to think about alternative approaches you might have used. Sections of recordings can be used as links between sessions or as triggers in future sessions. Even with a full transcription, an index or summary is very helpful. Usually a cassette or a CD copy (and sometimes a transcript) is given to the person who has done the recording.

Tape recorders are easy to use and most people quickly accept them. Experience shows that they inhibit very few people beyond the first few minutes of a session. Sound tape deteriorates over time unless kept in an even temperature. If you intend taping an interview, you need to have a clear agreement, before you begin, about what you intend to do, clarify who owns the record, how and when it may be used and where it is to be kept. Any reservations about access must be respected.

Read a guide to tape recorders and tape recording before starting. Either poor-quality recorders or poor recording techniques produce unusable recordings. Many of the pitfalls can be readily overcome with some simple instruction and practice. Many libraries, local radio stations, museums with sound archives and local history societies are so interested in obtaining oral recordings that they will often lend or hire tape recorders. In return, tapes will be stored in proper archival conditions, preventing deterioration, and the donor will receive a copy.

Guidelines for making audio recordings

When making an audio recording:

- use as good a machine as you can afford, preferably one with a noise reduction system;
- digital recorders and transcription software are increasingly available;
- use an external microphone rather than relying on an in-built one;
- if using cassettes, C60 or C90 cassettes are more robust;
- choose a quiet place without background noise, preferably a room with soft furnishings;
- learn to work the recorder and practise before starting to record a reminiscence session;
- check and adjust sound and volume levels;
- place the recorder within about 18–24 inches of the person. Better still, use a lapel microphone when recording an individual;
- use a multi-directional microphone for recording groups;
- if using a microphone on a stand, do not place it on the same surface as the recorder;
- plan the interview or group session with care – have a list of prepared questions to use as a guide;
- learn to ask only one question at a time and do not interrupt;
- ask different types of questions, including open or descriptive, specific or factual, and questions about related feelings;
- write identifying details giving name, location and date on the cassette or CD and on its box;

- keep an index of topics or a summary written as soon as possible after the interview.

Video recording

As video cameras and camcorders have become smaller and less intrusive, their usefulness in reminiscence work has greatly increased. Editing software now makes it much easier to produce video films of reasonable quality with less intrusive equipment and less expenditure of time. Remember that it is much more intimidating to be filmed than to be recorded on sound tape and free consent must be obtained. Remember too that we are all so accustomed to high-quality television that poor-quality amateur video film gives little pleasure or satisfaction.

A video shot of a person talking to camera or to an interviewer for more than a few minutes usually becomes rather boring unless action or movement can be incorporated or illustrative still photographs inserted. For a time-limited project it may be possible to obtain technical assistance from media studies students from local colleges but you will need to spend time in preparation during which the purpose, methods, content and outcomes of the project are clarified and agreed. Video clips have become more versatile and accessible, as they can be incorporated into multi-media presentations for viewing on computers, CDs and DVDs.

Using computer technology for producing life stories

Increasing numbers of older people are becoming computer literate and the opportunities for them to acquire information technology skills and access to computers is steadily growing (Sherman 2004). Unfortunately, too many ageing people still lack these skills, and strenuous efforts are needed to spread computer literacy. For the growing number of retired people who can use a PC, however, there are limitless opportunities for transforming their recollections into attractive, accessible permanent accounts. Many older people are using email and the Internet to share life history and reminiscence presentations across national and generational boundaries (Aldridge 2003). The gains from the cognitive exercise provided by recalling, rehearsing, organising and transferring memories into multi-media formats can be as valuable an investment in health and well-being as is taking regular physical exercise.

Provided older learners have access to support as they learn and are highly motivated to work on a task that is important to them, such as writing their family history or their life story, they are quite capable of acquiring information technology skills. They are also likely to need more instruction and practice initially and so may take longer to learn than younger people.

When introducing older learners to computers, the following guidelines are important:

- a relaxed, informal teaching style is essential to allay computer anxiety;
- much encouragement and reassurance is necessary, especially in the early stages, until confidence is established;
- computers need to be demystified and technical language used very sparingly and only in response to students' questions;
- being in a class with younger people is uncomfortable until basic computer competence has been achieved; mixed age groups are then more acceptable and often helpful;
- in the early stage of learning, twice-weekly sessions are recommended;
- ready access to a computer for additional practice in between sessions is helpful;
- open-learning manuals or notes enable each student to work at their own pace;
- a non-competitive, cooperative, sociable learning environment encourages older students;
- motivation is increased by early and frequent evidence of achievement in the form of hard copy or PowerPoint presentations;
- informal assistance from older mentors is most acceptable and much appreciated;
- a club rather than a classroom ethos has wide appeal and increases motivation.

Teaching older people to be responsible for their own writing and its production in an attractive format by means of desktop publishing has limitless possibilities. Acquiring computer skills and using them to accomplish reminiscence and life story work, or other tasks of personal significance, can be genuinely empowering.

Some people are content to write their reminiscences for their own private consumption, many write for their families. Others are driven by a desire to publish. Reminiscence-related writing is a complex process and its success depends on a number of factors. These include:

- present circumstances;
- the passage of time and how it relates to present circumstances;
- the intensity of emotion associated with the original memories and their recent recall;
- the effects of rehearsal on memories;
- the need to reconstruct the recalled memories so that they fit with the writer's present ideas about themselves, how they wish to be perceived by others and the meanings they now attach to their lives.

What people record, write and make public encourages others to begin to write. Much autobiographical writing occurs in private without the validating response of other people as experienced in a guided autobiographical writing group. The Internet has opened up access to a virtual audience for exchanging memories via reminiscence chatrooms. It also provides a ready outlet for people to create their own home pages to share their life stories and publicise their creative writing. Reminiscence using the Internet as a means for linking frail and isolated people has many possibilities, which health and social care workers seeking to achieve health gain and improved well-being are only slowly beginning to explore (Sampson 2004).

Microsoft PowerPoint life story presentations using CDs and DVDs

The major motivation for compiling multi-media presentations of life histories is the wish to leave behind a record, most often for the benefit of the family. Related purposes are the achievement of greater personal understanding through life review and the attainment of wisdom. These same formats can also be used to access relevant personal triggers to stimulate autobiographical memories and promote conversation with people whose memories are being compromised by dementia or brain injury.

The following account draws on the work of Tom Pierce (2003), a psychologist who identified the five stages in compiling a PowerPoint life history presentation as:

1 selecting photographs (300–800 pictures are suggested);

2 scanning photographs;

3 recording digital audio files of reminiscence (7–8 hours of recordings are suggested);

4 compiling picture and audio files in PowerPoint;

5 creating and copying CDs containing the PowerPoint presentation.

Only relatively modest computer skills are required to enable people to make extensive audio recordings of significant people, places, events and reflections that are then matched to relevant photographs. Desirably the photographs and matched sound recordings should represent the person throughout their entire life from earliest childhood to the present.

Selecting photographs

Photographs of places and people not necessarily known to the compiler but which are significant for the family's history, for example great-grandparents and grandparents, can be included. The photographs are arranged chronologically and each is given a three-digit code from 001 to 100. This is important for matching the audio files to the correct pictures. The digital technology makes alterations, deletions and insertions possible. If, for example, a photograph needs to be inserted in between 020 and 021 it will be coded 020a to avoid renumbering all the photographs.

Scanning

Each photograph is then scanned and stored in a computer file format such as JPEG. This provides good-quality reproduction and is easily imported into PowerPoint or a digital photo-editing program such as Adobe PhotoShop. It is advisable to include the code number in the picture file name, the owner's initials and also a few key words of description to assist easy identification. If slides are to be scanned, an additional slide attachment is required.

Audio recordings

These may be made in private but more and richer memories are likely to be evoked if the stories are recounted to one or more people. Prompting and questions can encourage elaboration and more detailed recall. A digital audio recording requires a computer with a sound card, a microphone that plugs into the sound card and editing software. A digital audio file should contain the same code number as the matched photograph. Pierce (2003) advises that MP3 format is adequate for storing the digital files.

PowerPoint

This enables text, photographs, recorded audio and video to be incorporated into a single presentation. Pictures and text can be arranged in many different styles and formats, and related audio and video files can then be linked. The presentation then resembles a slide show with commentary viewed on the computer screen or projected onto a larger screen if a data projector is available. Hyperlinks permit quick access to other slides so that it is easy to move, say, from a set of pictures of childhood to a set portraying adult life or sets of pictures of different locations lived in at various stages of life.

Copying to CD or DVD

Writing the PowerPoint presentation to a CD and creating a personalised label is then done so that the CD can be viewed on any computer equipped with a PowerPoint viewer facility. Digital storage means that multiple copies of a CD can be made – say, for giving to each family member. As the price of write-able DVDs drops, they will become useful substitutes for CDs because they will permit easy inclusion of video clips as well as increased storage capacity, which would enable several members of a family, for instance, to store their presentations on a single disk. The use of a DVD drive will enable presentations, not necessarily in PowerPoint, to be displayed on a television screen using a DVD player, which will dispense with the need for viewers to have a home computer.

Not everyone will wish to undertake the whole production process. Once having assembled the photographs and the audio and video recordings, in itself a worthwhile undertaking, a person may wish to hand over the technical aspects of production. Such facilitation and partnerships make excellent inter-generational projects that link older and younger people, provided that the participants have had adequate training in reminiscence work, have made careful preparations and a knowledgeable leader is available. If older people are helped to acquire and use the ICT skills required, and to share the technical aspects with younger partners, their satisfaction and self-esteem are likely to be considerably enhanced.

Increasingly, 'life historians' are offering similar services on a fee-paying basis. Attention to the process, including sensitive attention to the associated feelings aroused in the recall process, is pre-eminent even if the intention is to create a tangible product for personal, family or wider consumption.

Community archiving by older people and inter-generational groups

The creation of community archives by groups of older people or mixed age groups is another example of a tangible outcome of local and oral history, informed by personal reminiscences. The objective of such work is to create an Internet-accessible neighbourhood multi-media archive. In the process of working together on the archive, older people acquire multi-media skills and the archives they create become sources of local history, accessible to people of all ages. History and experience are preserved and the creation and use of the archive encourage personal, neighbourhood and community education and community development. (See Commanet (contact details in Appendix 2) for further information about community archiving.)

Ethical considerations

Reminiscence work with individuals, couples and groups raises a number of ethical concerns. Autonomy, choice, consent, respect for difference and ownership of outcomes have already been mentioned. Issues of fairness, benefit and risk are also relevant. By fairness is meant that each person has equal opportunity to participate and contribute according to their capacity, motivation and needs. The reminiscence experience should not harm but rather benefit the participant in the careful judgement of the worker. One of the biggest threats to the well-being of older people living in institutions of all kinds – and to many of those living in the community – that is seldom taken into account, is the risk of boredom. It saps vitality and erodes physical and mental health. It is therefore better to risk involvement in reminiscence activities than to do nothing to provide opportunities for stimulation and engagement, even if there is a small likelihood that an individual might be saddened or upset as a consequence.

Reminiscence workers, like oral historians, face the dilemma of whether it is ethical to talk with older people for the purpose of recording their recollections, and then, once done, abandoning them. There is no simple answer to this dilemma (Yow 1994). The guiding principle is founded on the idea of contract. It is better to be open, honest and explicit from the beginning about the purpose of any contact, the nature and likely duration of the relationship, and the nature of the hoped for outcomes. Most older people can accept time limits and time-limited relationships, painful as their ending may be. What they should not be asked to accept is being misled, used and then discarded.

In all such work, the process of engagement needs to be conducted ethically. So too does the production and use of any tangible outcomes that may also implicate other people who feature in the stories recounted. You need to be aware of and to take responsibility for the ethical ramifications of your reminiscence work and to try in every possible way to achieve informed consent on the part of all participants. This consent needs to include an agreement about any tangible outcome, where it will be kept and who may have access to it. Written consent is preferable to verbal consent, and Appendix 1 contains a sample consent form.

Conclusion

Many different ways of undertaking reminiscence with individuals and couples have been described, including simple reminiscence, structured life review and combined individual and group work used in guided autobiographical writing. Advances in information and computer technology have greatly increased the scope and ease of producing attractive tangible records in a number of different formats, and increasingly older people are taking advantage of these new possibilities to create records for their own, their families' and their communities' benefit.

KEY POINTS

- The interaction of inheritance, life history and present circumstances influences current troubling and troubled behaviour.

- Many individuals and their families are enriched both by the process of making a tangible life history record and by the record itself.

- The record can be presented in various formats, depending on the objectives to be served, and the interests, energy, expertise and resources available in making it.

- The 'product' belongs to the person; their ownership must be respected.

- The worker must behave ethically concerning the means and ends, the process and the product.

Application exercises

1 Write down five key words that relate to this chapter. Now write down why these words are important to your work with individuals or couples.

2 What more do you need to learn about or follow up as a result of having read this chapter?

3 Assist someone to make a tangible record of his or her life story.

Further reading

Birren JE and Deutchman D. (2005) 'Guided autobiography groups', in BK Haight and F Gibson (Eds). *Burnside's Working with Older People: Group process and techniques.* Boston: Jones and Bartlett

Haight BK, Coleman P and Lord K. (1995) 'The linchpins of a successful life review: structure, evaluation and individuality', in BK Haight and JD Webster (Eds). *The Art and Science of Reminiscence: Theory, research, methods and applications.* Washington DC: Taylor and Francis, pages 179–192

Sherman J. (2004) *Getting the Most Out of Your Computer.* London: Age Concern

7 Reminiscence and oral history in community development

Learning outcomes

After studying this chapter you should be able to:

- explain the use of reminiscence and oral history as tools for promoting community development, understanding community conflict, and promoting social inclusion and mutual understanding
- understand how to apply reminiscence skills to encourage community cohesion and lessen suspicion between groups
- identify the actions required to implement reminiscence practice in community contexts
- appreciate the values that should inform this work

Wider community applications of reminiscence and oral history

So far you have learnt about doing reminiscence work with individuals, couples and small groups for purposes that mostly benefit each individual involved. This chapter considers how to adapt and expand this knowledge and skills to benefit a larger number of people. Private troubles or personal problems are redefined as public issues when a group of people realise that they, and probably other people, share common concerns or face shared issues that require to be addressed in a more public way. Reminiscence and oral history share some characteristics while having some differences of emphasis and outcome. Major similarities and differences are summarised in Table 7.1.

Table 7.1 Comparisons between oral history and reminiscence work

Oral history	Reminiscence
Intended to preserve and transmit knowledge	Intended to benefit the individual
Major emphasis on outcome product	Major emphasis on relationships Secondary interest sometimes on a product
Semi-structured interview with prepared questions on a defined topic	Interactive, less structured, less interrogative and more responsive and open-ended
Done by history students and oral historians	Done by many different health and care professionals, oral historians and arts workers
Usually done with individuals although sometimes in small groups	Usually done in small groups and also with individuals and couples
Ownership usually passes to the interviewer	Ownership is open to negotiation
Power is vested with the interviewer	Power is vested in participants
Interviewer sets the agenda and directs the session	Facilitator negotiates a mutually agreed agenda
Legitimises the telling of personal stories and seeks to connect these with documented history	Celebrates personal stories and is usually less concerned to locate individual accounts within public history
Growing awareness of ethical issues	Awareness of and sensitivity to ethical issues
Uses various oral and documentary sources to check veracity and accuracy of accounts	Less concerned with truth telling and historical accuracy – more concerned with understanding what the story means to its teller

Oral history	Reminiscence
Always uses audio or video recording and note taking occurs during an interview	Does not always make an audio, video or written record, although will usually make some notes, often after a meeting
Seldom uses multi-sensory prompts	Frequently uses multi-sensory prompts
Interviews are frequently done in people's own homes, schools, museums or libraries	Located in many different domestic and community venues, including health and social care facilities

Source: Adapted from Bornat (2001) and Gibson (2004)

'Community development' refers to a process that seeks to encourage social justice, citizenship, participation, empowerment, advocacy, self-help and collective action primarily, but not always, by impoverished, marginalised or socially disadvantaged groups. It seeks to develop skills, to build capacities and, by promoting networking and cooperative action, to help people and communities to realise their potential. It challenges prejudice, racism, sectarianism and unequal distribution of and access to resources. Communities are encouraged to identify and to tackle problems that are recognised as important at a local level, and to build partnerships with private, statutory and voluntary agencies in order to acquire the skills and resources needed to overcome them.

The groups involved in such work will be connected because of where they live and the needs of their local neighbourhood or larger community. Sometimes they consist of people who share a common interest, characteristic or issue such as ethnicity, disability or special need, although they may not live close to each other. This sort of grouping is known as a community of interest rather than a locality-based or geographically based group. By working together, groups defined either by locality or by interest seek to benefit more people than themselves, their families or those with whom they live in a housing, health or care facility. This does not exclude benefit for group members and others with whom participants are personally connected but the objective is to benefit or improve conditions and quality of life for others as well, who may not be directly involved in the process.

Much of the earlier material concerning reminiscence work is relevant to its use in community development contexts but some objectives and the nature of the contract are likely to be different. Community development is a set of activities or actions that assists individuals, groups and communities to achieve positive social change for the public benefit. It challenges suspicion of difference, works to broaden opportunities for public participation and seeks to promote understanding between diverse people in order to promote the common good. It challenges racism, poverty, marginalisation and divisiveness and promotes social inclusion and responsible citizenship. It does not deny differences but rather seeks to celebrate, value and share both common and separate characteristics as a means of bringing about social change and development.

We too easily feel threatened by differences of age, class, culture, education, ethnicity, language, religion, sexual orientation, upbringing and values. We do not need to be captives of our heritage and history. If we are to live peaceably in a threatening world, understanding of difference and generosity towards others of divergent backgrounds are essential at community, national and international levels.

Learning from history

Oral history and reminiscence can make a considerable contribution towards enhancing community understanding and achieving the social inclusion of disparate groups. By assisting individuals to discover and value their own history and personal identity, it becomes more possible to reach out to others. Through sharing stories together, both different and common experience emerge. This can become the catalyst for shared effort in identifying and then solving problems – essential processes for building cohesive communities. Reminiscence with an oral history emphasis can never be the sole means used in community development. It can, however, make a very worthwhile contribution in terms of understanding the local context, the backgrounds of the individuals involved and the problems requiring attention, and building community capacity in order to address them.

If we can understand the past, we are more likely to better understand the present and to be free to plan for the future. Making comparisons between the past and the present seems to be a natural response when we experience moderate stress in the present, regardless of our age or the type of threat. This stress stimulates problem-solving. If anxiety becomes too great when faced with overwhelming stress, individuals and groups may need assistance in order to trigger recall, to remember past coping and to be able to make and to learn from such past and present comparisons. If individuals and groups fail to learn from the past, they are likely to experience the present as threatening, be fearful of the future and liable to repeat the mistakes of the past.

Characteristics of community-based reminiscence workers

Reminiscence and oral history projects located in community contexts seek to encourage exploration of the past, including dominant attitudes, values and behaviour. They facilitate change or modification through exploring personal, group and communal folk memories that separate and alienate people from one another. Doing history with community groups requires workers to be:

- secure in their own identity – aware of the impact of their own history and personal, cultural and political values;
- unthreatened by difference;
- confident in handling conflict;
- willing to hold people to the exploration of memories, no matter how painful;
- able to think critically and be open to new perspectives;
- sufficiently secure to question informants and the partisan views they are expressing;
- willing to question the role of history, oral history and reminiscence work;
- confident in challenging conventional powerful, prevailing accounts of history;

- able to ensure that conflicting accounts and different interpretations of history are heard;
- skilled in raising issues about representation and the impact of the stories on others;
- able to assist participants to understand that there is more than one version of a story, even if one version predominates;
- to encourage people to examine their own views of history, especially if they come to accept a view that differs from the dominant one;
- to negotiate how material will be represented and how discordant voices can also be heard.

Networking

Networking is the cornerstone of effective community development work. This is particularly relevant to reminiscence and oral history work within a community development framework. Building effective relationships with individuals and partnerships with community groups and statutory, voluntary and private organisations are essential skills (Carnwell and Buchanan 2004). This requires getting to know the community, its formal and informal organisations and their leaders, the economic, social and health needs of the area, and existing resources and how they are distributed. Involving other agencies in partnership projects requires a basic knowledge of key people and relevant organisations. A starter list should include community groups, health, social care, arts, religious and cultural organisations, libraries, museums, schools and colleges, and local business leaders, politicians and municipal officials.

Initially it is helpful to think in broad terms and then systematically refine your search for people from other organisations in terms of what social problem, issue or concern you wish to address. Think of a series of concentric circles as in Figure 7.1 – the inner one representing a group of people or a neighbourhood with a problem (or problems) that requires attention.

Figure 7.1 Identifying and locating community resources

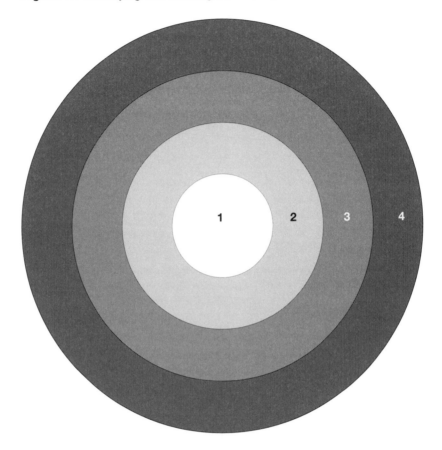

Key: **1** Group with interest, issue or problem for work

2 Local neighbourhood resources

3 Regional resource organisations

4 National resource organisations

As you meet with the group, begin to identify, in ever-widening circles, relevant resource organisations and key people within them who may be interested in working in partnership with you.

Enhancing practice through developing partnerships

Many professionals find that one of the most attractive aspects of reminiscence groupwork is its wide appeal to members of many different professions and occupations. It provides wonderfully rich opportunities for mixing with, learning from and being challenged by people whose training and working experience may be very different from your own. Initially this may be disconcerting and less comfortable and straightforward than choosing to work with a familiar person of similar background. Multi-disciplinary and inter-agency collaboration can be very fruitful although learning to work cooperatively across boundaries usually requires considerable effort. Relationships grow from purposeful work shared with mutually respectful and responsible partners. This does not mean that everyone is equal in terms of knowledge, skills, experience or responsibilities. It does mean, however, that there is clarity and explicit understanding about the contribution expected from each person in the team, and the resources they can bring, be they a professional or a volunteer, a senior practitioner or a new worker.

A mixture of workers from various backgrounds and agencies usually proves fruitful, and releases creative, imaginative ideas and novel ways of doing reminiscence. Librarians, museum staff, health and social care practitioners and community workers frequently pool resources and collaborate productively. Housing staff, teachers and community arts workers contribute immensely to the success of reminiscence work. Volunteers, including older people, are especially valuable. Their participation can be a reassurance to participants with whom they readily identify and are able to empathise with their special needs and possible limitations or disabilities. Volunteers must be given pivotal responsibilities and not left to feel undervalued – just invited along to make the tea or provide the transport, as important as these tasks are.

Oral history and reminiscence have been used in many different countries and for exploring and clarifying many different types of communal problems or issues. Some examples include efforts designed to challenge sectarianism and foster cross-community relations and mutual understanding in Northern Ireland, establishing land rights by Aboriginal people of Australia, integrating successive waves of immigrant groups in

New York and seeking to reconcile past wrongs in post-apartheid South Africa (Gibson 2004).

Conclusion

Reminiscence used in oral history work promotes community development objectives that encourage people to reflect upon their personal and communal memories in efforts to understand, reconstruct and reconcile conflicting representations of history. The process is intended to inform members of community partnerships or networks in their efforts to overcome present problems and meet the identified needs of local communities and their citizens.

KEY POINTS

■ Reminiscence and oral history have overlapping objectives, methods and values.

■ Communities, whether constituted by shared geography or by commitment to seeking improvements or change concerning common issues or shared needs, use reminiscence and oral history as vehicles for sharing past experience and engaging in problem-solving in the present.

■ Additional networking skills are needed to engage in effective community work.

■ Working in cooperative community-wide partnerships can be more effective than working in isolation.

Application exercises

1 Identify a concern or problem raised by an individual, or a family or a small group that may have similar implications for other people. Consider what relevance oral history or reminiscence may have in seeking a solution.

2 Can you identify any other resource organisations and key people that are accessible to you whose help you could solicit in undertaking an oral history project?

3 List the possible advantages and disadvantages of seeking and obtaining their involvement as partners in a reminiscence project designed to achieve an identified community objective.

Further reading

Nuttall S and Coetzee C (Eds). (1998) *The Making of History in South Africa.* Oxford: Oxford University Press

Popple K. (1995) *Analysing Community Work: Its theory and practice.* Maidenhead: Open University

Popple K, Quinney A and Jeffs T. (2005) *An Introduction to Community: An interdisciplinary guide to policy and practice.* Maidenhead: Open University/McGraw-Hill

Thompson P. (2000) *The Voice of the Past.* Oxford: Oxford University Press

8 Reminiscence with people from minority ethnic groups

Learning outcomes

After studying this chapter you should be able to:

- list reasons why reminiscence with minority ethnic elders is valuable
- understand why it is important to be aware of cultural differences towards ageing, death and dying
- understand the challenges faced by people who are growing old in a second homeland
- explain the importance of bearing witness to personal, family and group experiences
- identify the advantages and complexities of black and white co-working in groups with a membership drawn from different ethnic backgrounds.

Acquiring background knowledge

To be an effective reminiscence worker with people from minority ethnic groups it is important to learn about their history, religion, values, beliefs, customs and traditions. Broad general knowledge can only provide a background, for there are innumerable differences both within and between ethnic groups. Before starting any group it is important to be as well informed as possible about the likely origins and possible experiences of the people with whom you plan to work (see Chapters 4 and 5). But however much you have read or found out, it is essential to remember that what you 'know' may not apply to the individuals with whom you intend to work.

Some knowledge of British colonial history and twentieth century and current immigration and asylum policies is essential to understanding why people from various backgrounds now live in the UK and what significance this holds for them. Getting to know individual people from backgrounds that differ from your own will help prevent stereotyping. It will help you appreciate each person as a unique individual who is not just a member of a group to which you ascribe general characteristics. This cuts both ways. As you respect other people as individuals, so too you should expect that they will respect you as an individual.

The National Health Service, the local authority social services and other agencies caring for older people employ large numbers of staff drawn from minority ethnic groups. Their culture and often their religion will differ, possibly from the majority of their staff colleagues and the people for whom they are caring. Without these staff members many of the services would be unable to function effectively. Consequently, there is an obligation on service managers to ensure that staff members drawn from minority ethnic groups as well as service users from similar backgrounds are respected and appreciated. It is important that the majority of staff and care recipients are helped to understand and value the rich diversity that people from minority ethnic groups contribute to their care and well-being.

In all effective reminiscence work, respect for people, regardless of age, ethnicity, culture, religion, politics, gender and sexual orientation, is essential. Discriminatory attitudes and behaviour are unacceptable, and sensitive anti-discriminatory practice will be necessary if racism, or any other form of discrimination, surfaces in a reminiscence group.

Benefits from minority ethnic elders sharing their recollections

There are many reasons for encouraging minority ethnic elders to share their recollections but considerable sensitivity is necessary when doing so. Pam Schweitzer (1998a), artistic director, Age Exchange, suggests that reminiscence can:

- counter social isolation by developing two-way relationships and friendships;
- provide a tool for creating and preserving community identity;

- help to develop resource materials that are relevant to minority communities;
- keep a culture alive and vibrant by passing on learning, guidance and wisdom;
- give a sense of cultural identity for generations to come – for example, through passing on traditions such as story-telling;
- make connections across cultural, spiritual, generational and linguistic barriers;
- enable the voices of older minority people to be heard and appreciated;
- assist older people to claim and reclaim their own histories and heritage;
- overcome stereotypes and myths about minority ethnic elders;
- assist people to be known and appreciated as unique individuals;
- help to make services and service providers more responsive to minority needs.

It is important to appreciate that the reality of some people's experience in their new homeland may have turned out to be very different from what they were led to expect. They may also be reluctant to participate in groups with people they do not know, because they are fearful of eliciting prejudicial or racist responses if, by recounting their memories, they are critical about how they have been received. People of many different backgrounds may view discussion about religious beliefs, practices and political loyalties as divisive issues that they prefer to avoid. Care will be necessary in the choice of topics or themes proposed for reminiscence, especially for people who have migrated in order to escape torture, persecution, death and poverty. Some subjects may be too painful to contemplate discussing (see Chapters 1, 11 and 14).

Cultural differences towards ageing, death, dying and reminiscence

The experience of death is universal. How people react to death varies in innumerable ways, depending upon culture, religion, custom and conviction, informed by memory and re-enacted in experience.

Being invited to tell one's story is likely to evoke different responses in people from different ethnic backgrounds. For some it may be a natural thing to do, for others it may seem a strange or peculiar invitation. There may also be class, caste, gender, educational or income differences. For some people their past or present circumstances have been so painful that they do not wish to speak about them. So special sensitivity is required, and do not expect everyone to respond in the same way just because they belong to a minority ethnic group. Be prepared to appreciate individual and group differences as well as similarities between people within and between both minority and majority cultures.

If people share a common heritage, with common origins, language and values, reminiscence groupwork is likely to be more spontaneous than it might otherwise be in more heterogeneous groups. People who share a similar background will probably enjoy reminiscing with each other but reminiscence work in a group of people from different ethnic backgrounds is possible and often very desirable.

Reminiscence work as outlined in this book, with its emphasis on personal life history, albeit shared with others, may seem strangely Western and therefore alien or irrelevant to older people from some other cultural traditions. Not for everyone does the life lived give meaning to old age. Respect for elders and valuing the wisdom they have attained will be very important in some societies, but not in all. You will need to consider very carefully the culture and traditions of the people you wish to work with, and adapt the objectives, style and content of your reminiscence work accordingly.

Many white British and Asian elders, for example, approach old age and death differently. They do not view life satisfaction in the same way nor share the same ideas about the meaning of their own lives or the meaning of life in general. You must not expect everyone to believe or accept current dominant Western ideas. Many Westerners, for example, believe that there is one, and only one, life. Followers of some other faiths believe there are many previous and future lives (Henley and Schott 2004).

You also need to appreciate that other cultures have different views about how much people, as they age, should remain busily absorbed in everyday life. Contemplation rather than active engagement in late life is preferred in some cultures where withdrawal and seclusion rather than engagement and sociability are the norm. Disengagement rather than activity may be more desired.

In some Eastern religions a sense of personal fulfilment and absence of fear about the future, especially fear of death, is expressed more publicly, and religion is less private and personal than in the West. Older people from non-Christian backgrounds may find the Western emphasis on personal recollection and individual life history very odd and very self-centred. They may have a greater sense of community, of family, of being connected to others, and reminiscence work needs to be sensitive to these different traditions.

Growing old in a second homeland

The life story connects each of us to our 'place' and our own culture. If these connections have been disrupted for whatever reason – perhaps because of war, becoming a refugee, poverty, emigration or separation from home or family – it is particularly important to help people reconnect with their past and to be encouraged to remember significant relation-ships and once-familiar places.

Most of us who experience loss of significant places, even when freely chosen for positive rather than negative reasons, feel a kind of grief, or what Peter Read (1996) calls 'bereavement of place'. Our own awareness of lost places, near or far, of being 'strangers' in unfamiliar or even familiar surroundings or circumstances, of paths not taken or opportunities lost may help us to appreciate, in some small way, the sense of loss, anxiety and dislocation experienced by others.

Growing old in a second homeland, or growing old as a member of a min-ority ethnic group, even if born in Britain, may mean being disadvantaged and discriminated against in many different ways. Generally, people from all backgrounds who are healthy, well housed, have a close confidante and are economically secure do best in later life. Many immigrants, refugees and asylum seekers may experience poor health and poor housing and have had a long history of poorly paid employment or unemployment, which results in dependence on inadequate state benefits in old age. Many do not manage to get adequate help from the health and social services. Lack of English language skills will compound their problems. They may well feel insecure and isolated and be poorly provided for in late life. Having lost a homeland, they may not have gained a secure, respected place in their adopted country.

Group reminiscence for people from ethnic minorities may therefore be an important way of reconnecting them with their own communities and reaffirming their own historical and cultural roots. If managed sensitively, such work may help to convey a sense of respect, warmth and genuine interest in cultural diversity. It can help confirm both common and different characteristics and help people to value their life experience and cultural heritage. If workers are insensitive or treat people in ways experienced as or perceived to be disrespectful, the older person from a different background will feel hurt, isolated and demeaned.

As a care worker you may have some difficulty in empathising with the feelings of people who have grown old in a second homeland, especially if you are young and have not experienced immigration first hand. Alternatively, you too may belong to a minority ethnic group, even if you were born in Britain, and you may be experiencing a complex mixture of feelings concerned with your own and your family's cultural identities. Whatever our own origins and life experience, we all need to be open to learning about 'difference' and to appreciate how we feel and behave towards people who are 'different' from ourselves.

> 'We differ from one another in race, in national origin, in ethnicity, in gender, in sexual orientation, in beliefs, in political loyalties, in abilities, in personal histories, and in many other ways. These differences must be acknowledged and respected. The most profound and enduring truth is what we have in common, and what we have in common is our humanity.' (Lynn 2001, page 22)

Many immigrants, refugees and asylum seekers regard their new country with mixed feelings. Some may be proud and well satisfied with their achievements. For some, who might have experienced prolonged economic hardship, ill-health, racism and loneliness, living in Britain may have been an unhappy, unrewarding, lonely experience, now made worse by lack of adequate care in old age.

Some 'newcomers' may feel they have failed in their new land and that their hopes have not been realised, for many different reasons. They may experience a deep, probably unattainable, nostalgic longing to return to their homeland. Many realise the place they have left will no longer be the same, even if they could afford to return. Difficulties overcome, personal fulfilment and family success should be applauded. Reminiscence work uncovers pain but also provides many openings for affirmation, validation, encouragement and recognition of courage and achievement.

Immigration is not inevitably and universally perceived in terms of loss. Even in the face of much hardship endured, it will seldom be seen as totally negative. For very few migrants will life have been entirely negative. More often, leaving home, migrating, settling and growing old in a foreign land is spoken of with mixed feelings. These experiences are reported as a mixture of pain and pleasure, loss and gain, relinquishment and new beginnings. This ambivalence needs to be accepted and acknowledged.

Learning from minority ethnic group elders

It is essential for you to be finely tuned to the older person in the here and now; to understand what their present, as well as past, concerns are; and to be willing to share that experience, at the pace and in the ways in which the person wishes to recount it.

It is vitally important that you take the time and trouble to learn about different ethnic groups as well as to understand about the personal life experience of any particular individual. An effective way of gaining this knowledge is to listen attentively to older people from minority ethnic communities talking about their own homelands. Ask them questions, read, try to appreciate what life used to be like for them and in what ways it has changed.

Much of the fine detail of their stories will be affected by each individual's present circumstances and how receptive he or she perceives the audience to be. Careful selection of triggers will be necessary so that the homeland as well as the new land is represented. Families, community groups, churches, mosques, temples and synagogues, local radio stations and newspapers (including those serving minority ethnic groups), embassies, consulates, museums and libraries may be able to assist in locating culturally relevant triggers.

The same guidelines about group membership, good communication and building relationships already mentioned apply to work with members drawn from a single ethnic group or from various ethnic groups. If the leaders of a multi-ethnic group share the same background as some of the members, difficulties of communication and language will obviously be lessened. If you are a 'stranger', this is an opportunity for the older people to become your teacher in a very important sense.

There is likely to be only a very small number of people from any particular minority ethnic group in most day centres, care homes and hospitals. Nevertheless, even if small in number, their different needs concerning communication, information, food, hygiene, hair care, religious observance, health care, death and mourning customs and rituals need sensitive attention. *Culture, Religion and Patient Care in a Multi-ethnic Society* by Henley and Schott (2004) provides a wealth of relevant information.

Religious festivals such as Eid-ul-Fitr and Eid-ul-Adha (Moslem), Diwali and Holi (Hindu), and Passover and Hanukkah (Jewish) can provide opportunities for reminiscence about past celebrations in distant places and in adopted countries as well as being opportunities for valuing a person's special identity and extending others' understanding in the present. Celebrations using music, song, dance and food may be organised around important national Caribbean independence dates, Chinese New Year, St Patrick's Day, St David's Day, St Andrew's Day and many other special occasions. These special days and religious festivals for twelve major world religions are listed in the SHAP calendar (see Appendix 2), which is published annually together with an explanatory booklet.

Achieving cultural continuity by means of teaching and passing on traditions to inform and influence the next generation is very important in many reminiscence projects with people from minority ethnic groups. Reminiscence can also help in linking the past with the present and in problem-solving, relationship-building and coming to terms with life as it has turned out.

Reminiscence as problem-solving may be especially relevant to older people who live in care homes that are not finely tuned to individuals' cultural, dietary and religious needs, preferences and interests. Reminiscence could become a constructive, helpful means for recognising and drawing attention to different traditions and for influencing carers to respond more appropriately to the diverse needs and wishes of their residents or service users.

> **Day Centre Coordinator for the League of Jewish Women** *'Often, past lives were talked about for the first time in our reminiscence group. Non-Jewish staff could join in and make comparisons with their own past and tell of their own religious traditions. Probably the most important spin-off was the opportunity it gave to care staff and social workers to understand more about the different world their residents and clients had come from.'*

Reminiscence as life review may be too painful for some, but helpful for those who can bear to speak about their past experience, its joys and disappointments. They may have endured enormous loss and suffering, and it may take immigrants, asylum seekers or refugees longer to trust themselves to talk about their deepest concerns. Some may not wish to share their life review, for them a private process, particularly if they have had a hard struggle to come to terms with life's pain. Some may feel caught in a struggle to live life in two places, of wanting desperately to hang on to their old traditions while needing to accommodate to their present changed circumstances (Blackwell 2005). It may be helpful to refer back to the material in Chapter 3 concerning different types and styles of reminiscing.

The importance of bearing witness

Many immigrants and refugees have an overwhelming urge to 'bear witness'. For some, their pain has been so terrible, their loss so great, that it takes them many years to be able to face the enormity of their suffering. This has been seen most frequently, but not only, in Jewish survivors of the Nazi Holocaust. With continued wars, terrorism, famine, persecution, genocide, population displacement and disasters of many kinds in many parts of the world, similar reactions from increasing numbers of people to extreme trauma can be anticipated.

Some may find that no amount of telling can diminish their suffering, whereas others are quite unable to break their silence and speak of the unspeakable. 'Why was I spared?' or 'How could it happen?' may become recurring preoccupations in later life when there is more time for looking back and for introspective self-examination. Reminiscence in inter-generational family groups is particularly relevant although often very complex. Putting the record straight, telling it as it was by at last breaking the silence is one way of honouring the dead, validating the experience and justifying the survival of the witness. Such work is very demanding; it requires great skill and workers undertaking it require skilled supportive supervision.

Some writers have suggested that people who have endured terrible suffering or extreme trauma are sometimes unable to speak about it to their children but eventually, long after the event, are able to speak to their grandchildren. Hunt, Marshall and Rowlings (1997) give many case examples of people who in earlier life experienced various kinds of trauma that emerged only in late life or, for some, re-emerged in late life when being overtaken by dementia.

Always remember that some people manage to survive in the present only by forgetting the past; for them, remembering is to be avoided. Some descendants of survivors distance themselves from the stories of their elders – they do not or cannot bear to hear because they do not wish to carry the burdens of history; for them, making sense of the present is more important. We still have much to learn about the timing and the context in which traumatic life stories come to be told. It is, however, essential that, when the time comes to speak, there are skilled and sensitive listeners willing to hear the stories that people feel compelled to tell.

The possibilities and hazards of co-leadership

White reminiscence workers leading minority ethnic or mixed ethnic groups may unknowingly be perceived as dominating, condescending or oppressive, so they must take particular care to be well informed about the backgrounds of group members. They need to be aware of their own attitudes and prejudices, and to be sensitive and open to new learning.

Care worker *'We need to be aware of our own feelings. We need to be honest about how we feel about older people generally and race in particular if we are to ease some of the hurt.'*

Black and white co-working

Any co-working relationship is complex, as has already been explained in Chapter 4. Black and white co-working in groups is even more complex. It is another factor to be considered at the planning stage. What should be the mix of age, class and gender? Should the group and its leaders be all black, all white or mixed black and white? Some people, both black and white, question whether black/white co-working is ever possible or acceptable. It is important for you to know where you stand on such issues so that you are not caught out unawares when becoming involved in reminiscence groupwork. Mistry and Brown (1991), social work teachers, suggest that black/white co-worker pairing is usually desirable where the group is racially mixed and there are many potential benefits associated with joint working.

Co-working requires consideration of the following:

- Are you willing and able to model co-leadership?
- Have you agreed general ground rules?
- Decide how many workers to have. Should it be one, two or more?
- Is a black/white pair appropriate?
- Can you work comfortably with the particular person proposed?
- Do you agree over purpose, principles and practice?
- Are you able to talk openly about the ethnicity dimension of the partnership?
- Have you talked about issues of authority between yourselves and within the group?
- Have you agreed how racism will be handled in the group?

- Have you agreed how differences in background, aptitudes, age, skill, experience and ability are to be handled between the co-workers?

- Have you planned to share tasks on a fifty/fifty basis so that the white worker will not automatically be cast as the leader?

- Are you able to give each other feedback on performance? Can you be honest with each other?

- Have you agreed about supervision and consultation?

Overcoming barriers to effective work

The experience of immigrants will not be all the same, even though they all share the common elements of leaving, journeying, arriving and settling and the feeling of never completely belonging. To be old in Britain and to be Irish, Polish, Chinese, Asian, African, Somali or Caribbean will not be the same experience. Do not assume that reminiscing with one minority group will be any easier than reminiscing with another, just because you share a common first language. Shared language obviously helps but many other subtle factors are also important. Henley and Schott (2004) give much useful information on cultural, linguistic, religious and other ethnic differences as well as guidance about working with interpreters and the need to develop sensitivity to our own biases, prejudices and communication limitations.

Reminiscence groups that touch on the harsh realities of discrimination may be hard for white leaders and members to cope with because their own racial attitudes and national identity will be challenged. Accounts of racism and discrimination at work or school, abuse, pain, trauma, violence, and being refused accommodation and denied employment, educational opportunities or care which others take for granted, are liable to arouse guilt, defensiveness or denial. Both tellers and hearers of stories about such experiences will be touched in many different ways. People who have struggled all their lives to rise above grinding poverty and deprivation, for example, may not wish to be reminded of their own battles by hearing the stories of other people. Effective groupwork demands that feelings, no matter how painful and threatening, be openly talked about and honestly acknowledged.

Take particular care to overcome any language barriers in order to make it possible for people to participate in reminiscence work. Invitations and notices may need to be written in various languages, depending on who is to be invited. The most common languages and dialects encountered will probably be Punjabi, Hindi, Urdu, Gujerati, Kutchi, Bengali, Sylheti, Cantonese, Mandarin and patois.

Consider using interpreters. When looking for assistance with interpretation, begin within your own workplace. Do you have any colleagues who speak the required language and could be asked to help? If not, look elsewhere. Some local authorities provide an interpreter service. Many social services fieldwork teams have social workers from varied ethnic backgrounds. Volunteers could be sought in local community groups, language agencies and places of worship. Local schools and colleges may be delighted to work with you in order to open up opportunities for their pupils and staff to engage in community service or inter-generational learning projects.

Working successfully with an interpreter requires mutual trust and careful preparation. It is important that the interpreter understands the purpose of reminiscence generally and also the particular objectives of each group or project, and is in sympathy with the approach being used. The interpreter is essentially a co-worker or colleague. It is they who will need to bear the brunt of emotions expressed by the people reminiscing in addition to translating the content of the stories told. They may also be able to advise about suitable topics and themes, to suggest resource materials or to assist in locating appropriate triggers. For a detailed account of working with interpreters, see Henley and Schott (2004).

Conclusion

The courage, resilience and strength of older people, especially those from minority ethnic groups, need to be recognised and celebrated. Reminiscence as witnessing, teaching, problem-solving and stock-taking is important. It connects the person to their culture, both past and present. People whose lives have been disrupted by geographic dispersal, emigration and separation from home and family may find group reminiscence or individual life review particularly helpful. Some of this earlier experience of pain and loss may be mirrored in late life (and possibly reactivated for some) by the pain of other life events such as divorce, bereavement, ill-health and disability or admission to a care home or health facility. Reconnecting through reminiscence and recall of important past events, significant relationships and special places may make the present more agreeable or at least more tolerable.

Ethnically sensitive reminiscence work will not solve all the problems of inequality, racism, discrimination and social exclusion. It is, however, a way of challenging discrimination, extending mutual understanding and establishing warm, respectful, caring relationships. This will not happen automatically but only as we confront our own prejudice and become open to learning from people whose ethnicity, beliefs, language, religion, culture and life experience differ from our own. Small reminiscence groups and individual life story work offer a sympathetic climate in which this process might begin.

KEY POINTS

- Be alert to the possibility that you may be imposing your own culture and values on others.

- Develop your understanding of what it is like to grow old in a second homeland, through books, films, sensitive questioning and careful listening.

- Ethnically sensitive reminiscence work can help to inform about differences of age, class, culture, ethnicity, gender, religion and status.

- Cross-cultural groups can share common life experiences if not a shared cultural inheritance.

- Inter-generational and cross-cultural work can be rewarding for both older and younger people.

- Co-leadership in groups with a multi-cultural membership is commended.

Application exercises

1 Find an older person whose ethnic origins differ from your own. Ask if he or she will teach you about the important aspects of their own culture, especially attitudes and practices concerned with family life, age and ageing, death and dying.

2 Begin to develop a co-working relationship with a colleague whose ethnic background differs from your own. Try reading and then discussing together this chapter before commencing joint reminiscence work.

3 Plan some reminiscence work with an older person (or persons) from a minority ethnic group. Prepare a list of possible relevant multi-sensory triggers that are age, gender, geographically and culturally appropriate and where you might locate them.

Further reading

Alibhai-Brown Y. (1998) *Caring for Ethnic Minority Elders: A guide.* London: Age Concern

Henley A and Schott J. (2004) *Culture, Religion and Patient Care in a Multi-ethnic Society: A handbook for professionals.* London: Age Concern

Mistry T and Brown A (Eds). (1997) *Race and Groupwork.* London: Whiting and Birch

Schweitzer P (Ed). (1995) *Making Memories Matter: Reminiscence and intergenerational activities.* Papers from European Reminiscence Symposium. European Reminiscence Network. London: Age Exchange

Schweitzer P. (2004) *Mapping Memories: Reminiscence with ethnic minority elders.* London: Age Exchange

9 Inter-generational reminiscence work

Learning outcomes

After studying this chapter you should be able to:

- understand the opportunities and obstacles in undertaking reminiscence work with pairs and groups of mixed ages
- appreciate the importance of careful preparation for inter-generational reminiscence work
- formulate a tentative plan for an inter-generational reminiscence project
- embark on an inter-generational reminiscence project

The mutual benefits of inter-generational work

Inter-generational projects utilising older people as living resources, models and mentors are growing in popularity. Younger and older people who engage in inter-generational work report considerable benefits and satisfaction, once their initial anxieties have been overcome. Children of all ages and students in all kinds of schools, including children with special educational needs, benefit in many different ways from working directly with older people. Many projects build partnerships between schools and local health and social care facilities, including hospitals, care homes, day centres and community groups. Establishing effective working relationships between staff from educational and health care sectors requires time and meticulous attention. Mutual understanding, respect and affection grow out of shared experience – it seldom exists from the outset of a project.

A great deal of inter-generational work takes place within single-identity minority ethnic communities and is designed primarily for elders to teach younger people about the traditions and beliefs of their own culture. Members of majority communities also fruitfully engage in cross-generational work for the purposes of combating ageism, lessening mutual suspicion, building friendships and transmitting knowledge, experience and wisdom.

Some projects are both cross-cultural and inter-generational. The value of inter-generational projects is not limited to preserving and passing on skills and memories of people from minority ethnic groups, although the need for doing so may be felt more urgently within these communities. Mixing people of different ages and different ethnic and cultural backgrounds can be a particularly fruitful means for promoting trust between members of different communities.

Giving guidance and transmitting wisdom is frequently given as the major justification for older people's involvement in inter-generational work but the learning is never in one direction alone and should never be portrayed as such. Younger people may learn from older people but the reverse is also true and younger people have much to teach their elders. Older people may need assistance in appreciating the mutual benefits of the two-way learning that occurs in mixed-age groups while children may need to be encouraged to perceive themselves as both learners and teachers and not just as 'being nice to old people'.

The following quotations from Schweitzer (1993, page 7) illustrate these mutual benefits.

> **Lilian Burnett, school volunteer** *'You are giving them a little bit of your experience. You can tell them and explain it and they're really hanging on what you're saying, as long as you're telling the truth, that's the main thing. You must tell them the absolute truth.'*

> **Bill O'Rourke, school volunteer** *'Remember – because memories do matter, if we are not to forget our past, if we are to understand and respect one another, because the old are important and the young have things to learn from them.'*

Betty Green, a primary school pupil *'I love the days our friends from the day centre come to school – we all do things together and help each other. They tell us stories and then we usually draw together or we draw and they chat, and we tell them what games we play and sing our favourite songs, which they are now learning from us.'*

Older people comment very favourably about their participation in projects that cross age barriers, decrease their self-consciousness and improve their self-esteem.

Eileen O'Sullivan, school volunteer *'I find it gives me a lot of confidence when I tell the children my experience. I feel really great. I couldn't do that with grown-up people, but with children I come over well and I feel as though I have done something.'*

Projects vary in objectives, size, duration, complexity and resources. Some are undertaken within the school day as part of the National Curriculum whilst others use students' and older people's free time and may occur in a variety of venues, including youth clubs, community arts organisations, museums, care homes and people's own homes. Inter-generational reminiscence work can be adapted to suit all ages from kindergarten through primary, secondary and tertiary education levels. If the work takes place within an educational setting, it conveys to children and to older people that it is valued. If it takes place within a health or social care facility, it will convey messages of frailty and illness, hopefully tempered by resilience and an enduring capacity for having fun. If it takes place within a family, it recognises and contributes to family solidarity, affection and regard, and may have a longer-term impact in terms of developing caring relationships and mutual aid.

Inter-generational work takes many different forms and brings mutual social as well as educational benefits. Older people are able to share their knowledge of varied life experience, history, geography and other subjects with younger people, who appreciate hearing vivid authentic accounts of past times. Children are intrigued and captivated by hearing first-hand accounts of past times and events.

The importance of careful preparation

Careful preparation of everyone involved is essential. Separate preparation of both older and younger people is crucial to success. Only when each group has faced their apprehensions and shared their reservations will they be ready to meet each other. Preliminary exercises that promote exploration of stereotypes usually assist each group to develop trust and willingness to move into joint meetings.

In preparing the older informants for a school visit, a reminiscence session on the same theme as the intended school topic helps them to realise they have much to tell. By telling their own stories and listening to the stories of their peers, further memories will surface so that the eventual exchanges in school are likely to be much more detailed. Encourage the older people to visualise the children they will be meeting, to practise adapting the level and language of their stories accordingly and to respond to questions in expansive rather than limited ways. Bringing memorabilia to show the children can be very helpful, and also photographs of themselves as children at various ages, as these can provide an intriguing starting point for conversations.

Relationships take time to develop, so a number of contacts is usually more productive than a single visit. Children as well as the older people need help in preparing the topics or themes to be covered during a visit or, preferably, a series of visits; follow-up work by the children, if shared with the older informants, brings extended contacts, mutual pleasure and satisfaction.

Projects often begin with very modest objectives but, as people begin to enjoy their involvement, ideas develop and valued relationships, new knowledge, activities and tangible and intangible benefits emerge. Plays, musicals, exhibitions, events, outings, visits, entertainments, published stories, books and poems as well as conventional and email correspondence, friendship, increased understanding and shared respect have all developed out of inter-generational work.

The children will need to plan and prepare for receiving their guests. They will need courteously to welcome their visitors, provide refreshments if possible, show the older people around the classroom and ensure they have somewhere comfortable to sit and put their coats. The children too may need to practise asking questions beforehand, by interviewing each other and by learning to use open-ended questions instead of closed questions to explore agreed themes. Attentive listening and remembering are crucial, and both improve with practice. Children will also need to practise note taking, and possibly using a camera, tape recorder or video camera. With very young children, parents may be recruited as note takers. The classroom meeting then becomes a catalyst for further classroom activities of many different kinds.

Risk-taking in inter-generational reminiscence projects

Embarking on inter-generational projects requires a careful assessment of risks and opportunities, as it is essential that neither older nor younger people be put at risk or hurt in the process. Table 9.1 summarises the possible gains and losses that might be involved for both older and younger participants.

Table 9.1 Opportunities and risks for participants in inter-generational reminiscence projects

Opportunities	Hazards and risks
Relationship building through developing familiarity and trust – becoming friends	Increasing suspicion and distrust – alienation between older and younger people
Challenging age-related stereotypes	Confirming age-related stereotypes
Teaching the lessons of life – wisdom sharing	Rejecting the lessons of life
Transmitting cultural knowledge and history	Denying or rejecting cultural inheritance and history
Providing a role model	Rejecting of role model
Learning about contemporary life, interests, aspirations and experience	Lack of interest in learning about others' issues and concerns

If older people's recalled memories are not affirmed but instead are denied or dismissed because they do not coincide with the dominant accepted interpretation of history or are alien to the current concerns of society, this can be damaging and affect well-being. This may happen, for example, when the prevailing collective view of wartime does not coincide with the personal experience of an individual (Thomson 1998). Els Van Dongen (2005, page 525), an anthropologist, writes about the predicament of older disadvantaged black people in South African townships who in the Apartheid era experienced violence, inequality, disruption and poverty:

> 'Older people's memories of these experiences are not valued
> ... memories, rather than bringing the generations together,
> have the opposite effect and widen the gap in understanding
> between the older and younger generations ... the silencing
> of memories reflects the society's radical break with the past,
> which has made it difficult for younger people to mourn or
> sympathise with older people's losses.'

This contrasts starkly with other South African oral history projects that are actively soliciting people's memories, sometimes as family projects, and preserving and archiving them in many different formats (Denis and Makiwane 2003). If problems associated with inter-generational sharing are encountered, whether in community-based groups, care groups or families, alternative opportunities for elders to share their stories with fellow sufferers or with other receptive listeners must be offered.

It is equally important that the contribution of the younger participants in inter-generational projects is appreciated and that they too feel respected. Although there are hazards, many gains have been reported from inter-generational projects. Schweitzer's (1993) list of rewards for children and for older people from school-based work projects in London is summarised in Table 9.2.

Table 9.2 Summary of Schweitzer's rewards for children and for older people

Rewards for children	Rewards for older people
A change in the routine	Meeting and working alongside teachers
An air of excitement and expectancy	Stimulus of recalling their own school days in a classroom setting
Meeting new people in the classroom	
First-hand presentation of experience	Recognising change and continuity
Associating the past with living people	Appreciating the burdens and opportunities for children within contemporary education
Understanding similarities and changes over time	Being valued and appreciated for one's life experience
Testing beliefs and preconceptions	Realising the extent of one's own knowledge
Discovering new information	Passing on skills, knowledge and values
Positive reinforcement of curiosity	
Trying out new knowledge	Enjoying and appreciating the humour, playfulness and knowledge of children
Applying new understanding within own family	Recalling past pleasures and obstacles overcome
Handling unfamiliar objects	
Demonstrating newly learned skills	Providing access to stimulating triggers and other resources
Acting out ideas and experiences	Developing skills in responding to questions and imparting experience
Discovering humour, disbelief challenged	
Extending vocabulary and social confidence	

Rewards for children	Rewards for older people
Being respected by an older person	Being thanked and appreciated by children and teachers
Appreciation of their own educational experience	Forming friendships that might endure outside the classroom
Increased awareness of how different people cope	

Source: Adapted from Schweitzer (1993, pages 4–5)

Older people need to be recognised as the 'experts', although not infallible, as they recount their personal life experiences. This increases their self-esteem as they see themselves valued, respected and appreciated by the children. Each group learns from the other and, if working side by side over several weeks, older people develop greater awareness of modern educational methods, requirements and expectations that contemporary children and teachers face. This experience promotes recall and reconstruction of memories and encourages the older person to re-evaluate the past. Frequently this results in a more balanced reappraisal of their past and present lives, few continuing to believe uncritically 'that it was better in my day'.

The presence of older people in the classroom can permeate the whole curriculum. History, citizenship, language and literature, technology, geography, economics, nutrition, drama, art and music, social skills, religious education, values and morality are all areas of study that can benefit from inter-generational exchanges.

Emma Dean, a school girl *'It started as fun. It finished with us intrigued ... It was us who wanted to know and by asking the experts we found out. The experts at first made us nervous, now they are our friends. They've helped us and we hope we've given them our friendship and trust. I hope they feel the play is as much theirs as ours.'* (Schweitzer 1993, page 6)

In successful projects, however, the gains are recognised as mutual. An older volunteer school reminiscence worker spoke of the two-way benefits of inter-generational contacts and how important such sharing becomes to both the younger and the older person involved: 'We show them what they cannot get from books. Nobody can get it from a book, what we know. The day I go to school is the best day of my week.'

Locating interested older people requires time and effort in approaching local seniors' clubs, day centres, churches, temples, synagogues and mosques, care home facilities and sheltered housing. Build on existing relationships to open up possibilities for developing a collaborative project, and in joint meetings identify the mutual objectives, anticipated gains and possible obstacles for older and younger groups.

Brief older participants on child protection issues and have an explicitly agreed child protection policy in place. All of this takes time, including the possible security vetting of potential volunteers so that child-protection policies can be followed meticulously. The effort involved can bring rich rewards. Listening carefully to a young person's opinions, concerns and feelings without judging can generate a lifeline to self-respect. It can provide much-needed encouragement that the young person may otherwise lack.

Teaching skills for living through shared involvement

Older people's participation in classroom storytelling and writing projects encourages reflecting, sharing and writing by young children. Stelson and Dauk-Bleess (2003), elementary school teachers, believe that 'shared projects can change the lives of children, deepen the community spirit of the classroom and expand empathy beyond the classroom walls' (page 40). They begin such writing projects by encouraging the children to brainstorm memories with an older partner and to jot down as many different memories as possible. The children then select three possibilities from their lists by asking themselves a series of reflective questions:

- Which experience can I see like a movie?
- Can I remember how I felt at the time?
- Am I willing to re-live the experience?
- Am I willing to make the memory public?

- Which memory says 'write about me'?

The children next try to recapture the intensity of the memories by briefly telling the three stories to their older partner who asks the child 'What is the hotspot of the story?' and 'Why is this experience important to you?' This process helps the child to choose the story he or she is willing to 're-live on paper' and the actual story writing begins. Through this staged process of recalling memories, the children are helped to learn a structure and a method for future narrative writing and reflection. These children are beginning to learn in childhood how to recall, recapture and reappraise memories of their life experience rather than waiting until late life to begin to acquire these skills.

Ethnic community groups have much to contribute to inter-generational reminiscence work. Liz Bartlett (1992), Coordinator of the Kensington and Chelsea Community History Group, now called History Talk, illustrates the dynamic nature of such work in her account of a lunch club for African-Caribbean community elders:

> *'The topic – food – in one reminiscence session developed over time into a book with the title* Nice Tastin': Life and food in the Caribbean. *Members of the club went in every week to two classes in a nearby primary school, where they passed on some of their knowledge of the culture. The children responded by producing wonderful drawings of Caribbean fruits and vegetables; they learnt how to cook potato pone, and they especially enjoyed story-reading and story-telling sessions.'*

Having older people from different cultural or religious groups serve as culturally sensitive informants assists understanding of distant places as well as life in local ethnic communities. They can speak authentically about their different origins and backgrounds as well as their experience of discrimination and cultural misunderstandings. Skills for life can be learned from authentic accounts of domestic life, work and working conditions, transport, medical services and many other topics. These can be explored productively in myriad ways when older and younger people of all ages share their ideas together.

Schweitzer (2004, page 39) suggests:

'For children and grandchildren of immigrants, a sense of personal and community history is especially important in building self-esteem. Older people have a very positive role to play here, reinforcing a cultural legacy, passing on personal stories and customs, and stimulating children in their communities to be interested in their own family "histories".'

Projects located within health and social care facilities

These also have much to commend them but they 'feel' very different from school-based work. Here it is more difficult to develop true mutuality because the older people are likely to be frail, much less independent and more likely to confirm younger people's stereotypical ideas about being old, frail and excluded from the mainstream of life. The environment will suggest less mutuality and promote any latent tendencies in the young people to bestow their beneficence rather than be mutual partners in a shared enterprise. They are more likely to see themselves as doing good, as entertainers rather than learners. With careful preparation and skilled implementation, prior stereotypes of both groups can be replaced by greater openness, mutual appreciation and genuinely shared pleasure.

Grandparent involvement

Many schools run grandparent projects, and if children do not have grandparents they are encouraged to involve other older relatives or friends. Face-to-face contact is recommended but email and Internet use now overcome some of the disadvantages associated with modern, dispersed nuclear families. In these sorts of family-based projects children are usually set the task of interviewing the grandparents about previously agreed issues. This approach is more akin to an oral history project in which questions designed to prompt the collection of information relating to a particular topic or theme are used for a narrowly defined purpose. Such interviews are inclined to be less wide ranging than a group discussion. They are more focused and more likely to elicit knowledge rather than experience informed by the personal values of the older person. On the other hand, individual interviews accelerate relationship building, and intimacy, trust and friendship may develop more quickly than in a group. A combination of working in pairs and in small groups usually proves very fruitful.

Visiting classrooms, watching history films together and joining in the ensuing discussion is always productive. Audio and video recordings, photographs and published reminiscence accounts provide an excellent basis for drama. Using one person's life story to develop awareness of social and economic changes over time provides a focused appreciation of personal experience located within a wider historical context. Unpacking memory boxes together and using local older people as guides for visits, excursions or trips to local historical sites and museums introduce varied personal points of view.

'I was there when …' brings history alive – it transports us to another time and place. We hear a first-hand witness telling us how it was – and we are intrigued, fascinated, hooked and moved beyond our wildest imaginings. As past times come alive, we respond and are changed subtly and sometimes dramatically. (See also Chapters 7 and 8.)

Conclusion

This chapter and the two previous ones are concerned with encouraging people of different ages, backgrounds and circumstances to use their memories of past times, places, people and events for crossing boundaries and lessening the distance between themselves and other people. Although differences divide, we are united by our common humanity if only we feel free to embrace it. Differences are not denied. On the contrary, reminiscence and recall seek to celebrate difference but also to discover shared experience in order to foster mutual understanding and acceptance. The past then becomes a bridge to the present and a way of creating opportunities to bring people closer together.

KEY POINTS

- Inter-generational work takes place in many different settings in educational, health and social care and community contexts.

- It can involve children and young people of varied ages working alongside older people.

- It requires meticulous separate and joint preparation of all participants.

- It is best spread out over a number of sessions to enable relationships to grow and practical work to be developed.

- Effective work requires that the contributions of both younger and older people are validated and respected.

Application exercises

1 Explore the possibility of initiating an inter-generational reminiscence project in the place where you work. Identify possible objectives, participants, partners, likely gains, risks and outcomes.

2 Ask a small number of older people about themselves when young. Ask them to identify their teenage hopes and fears and to suggest what contemporary teenagers might say about their hopes and fears today.

3 List what would encourage/discourage you from embarking on an inter-generational project.

Further reading

Golden S and Perlstein S. (2004) *Legacy Works: Transforming memory into visual art.* New York: Elders Share the Arts

McCrea JM and Smith TB. (1997) 'Types and models of inter-generational programs', in S Newman et al (Eds). *Intergenerational Programs: Past, present and future.* Washington, DC: Taylor and Francis; pages 81–93

Perlstein S and Bliss J. (2003) *Generating Community: Intergenerational partnerships through the expressive arts.* New York: Elders Share the Arts

Savill D. (2002) *A Time to Share: Powerful personal stories for teaching history and citizenship.* London: Age Exchange

10 Reminiscence with people who have dementia and their carers

Learning outcomes

After studying this chapter you should be able to:

- understand about the complexity of dementing conditions
- realise how dementia affects the person with dementia, their family and paid carers
- improve communication with people with dementia by adapting reminiscence techniques
- appreciate the similarities and differences between reminiscence, reality orientation and validation therapy
- adapt reminiscence for individuals, families and small groups affected by dementia

Understanding dementia

Family and professional carers, friends and neighbours all find that dementia stretches our understanding, patience, perseverance and love. Dementia challenges us to find ways of staying in touch, in relationship, of continuing to communicate because the person who develops dementia still remains a person who requires our love, concern and respect. Too often pessimism, stigma, fatigue and fear leave people with dementia and their family carers unsupported and increasingly isolated as deterioration inevitably increases and dependency grows.

'Dementia' is an umbrella term for a syndrome that refers to a collection of progressive organic diseases of the brain, not to a single disease, which while usually sparing physical health affects cognitive, emotional and social aspects of functioning. Ageing is the biggest single risk factor for developing dementia, so our increasingly ageing population makes it one of the major health issues of the present time. The symptoms include progressive inability to undertake the ordinary affairs of daily life because of severe and progressive decline in memory, reasoning, comprehension, learning capacity, judgement and problem-solving. Social behaviour, emotional control, language, orientation and vitality are usually affected, and depression and anxiety are also common. Dementia is not an inevitable consequence of ageing and is different from age-related minor forgetfulness. Most, but not all, dementias overtake people in later life. A small number of people, however, develop dementia in mid-life or even earlier. The chances of being affected increase considerably from approximately three in every 100 people over 65 years of age to between ten and fifteen in every 100 people over 80 (Burns, Dening and Lawlor 2002).

Definitions, diagnosis and assessment methods are not standardised. There is no definitive diagnostic test (except at post-mortem) although imaging procedures and accurate history taking are improving assessments. It is therefore difficult to calculate accurately the number of people with dementia. In the UK some 600,000 people are thought to have dementia. The numbers are growing because, as more people live longer, the number with dementia increases. Dementia seems to occur in all countries and affects people regardless of gender, social class, income and ethnic group, although it has been suggested that a higher level of education and continuing physical and cognitive exercise and stimulation offer some protection.

Research into the causes of dementia continues. Although various factors are implicated in the neurological deterioration that occurs, how any one person is affected depends on a complicated mix of physical factors, life experience, psychological factors (including unresolved past trauma), social interactions, emotional security and present circumstances. It is possible to have more than one type of dementia simultaneously, and distinctions between different types are not always clear cut. Drugs that improve some people's symptoms and well-being at least for a time are now available, so early diagnosis is vital to gain access to these treatments and to other supportive services.

Alzheimer's disease is the most common dementia and people often use this term loosely to refer to all dementias, no matter what their type or cause. Alzheimer's disease and Lewy body dementia have no known cure, the cause is uncertain and the progression variable. They probably account for well over 50 per cent of all cases. Vascular dementia is another common type, caused by repeated small strokes or haemorrhages in the brain. Preventive health measures such as good diet and exercise throughout life and treatment for high blood pressure may assist prevention to some extent. Other dementias include those associated with excessive use of alcohol, AIDS, Creutzfeldt–Jakob disease (CJD), Parkinson's and stroke.

Person-centred care emphasises the importance of understanding the multiple factors, past and present, that contribute to any individual's unique pathway through the experience of dementia. There are neurological, psychological and social aspects to dementia that help to account for how different people are affected. As a progressive, chronic, terminal illness, usually lasting for many years, dementia makes heavy demands on family carers, who are most often older spouses or partners. Family carers are entitled to an assessment of their own needs and they will usually require information, respite and various domiciliary and supportive services as the demands made upon them change and increase over time.

It is important, but not always easy, to distinguish between dementia and depression, as many of the symptoms seem to be similar. Depression frequently goes undiagnosed and untreated. Depression in earlier life seems to increase the likelihood of dementia in later life but, for many people who have dementia, depression and anxiety are normal responses to this abnormal condition. The memory and learning problems associated with dementia often resemble depression. The low mood, apathy, withdrawal and poor self-care seen in depression are also common in dementia. The ways in which mental and physical health are affected in dementia, together with accompanying behavioural, mood and memory changes, and the speed of deterioration vary greatly from person to person.

The term 'confusion' is often used instead of 'dementia'. Confusion is a symptom, rather than a disease. Many people with a dementing illness are indeed 'confused' about themselves, other people, where they are and even the time of day. Except in the very advanced stages, people with dementia are seldom totally confused. They may be clear about some things and very mixed up about others. Some die early, others live for many years. Some people's behaviour may be very difficult and demanding, beyond their control. Yet there are others who, if treated in ways that meet their individual needs for care, security, respect and freedom from stress, are able to function reasonably well long into their illness.

In the early stages of dementia, as people become increasingly aware of their failing memory, many feel anxious, agitated, restless and depressed. Other losses and life changes, especially losing a spouse or partner or moving to an unfamiliar environment, will make their problems more visible and may also accelerate decline. As the disease develops, people find it hard, but not always impossible, to learn new skills or retain information, to remember recent events or recall old information on demand, to hold a coherent conversation and to manage personal and domestic affairs, including personal hygiene. They are unaware of danger, get lost in familiar places, become unable to make decisions or to plan ahead. At times their behaviour can cause embarrassment and offence. As the disease progresses, they are likely to grow more withdrawn and isolated, cut off from others, who may be slow to realise initially that something serious is wrong.

Often relatives, friends and neighbours feel that the person with early dementia is just being difficult. As deterioration continues, both professional and family carers need to find ways of dealing with their own anxiety – will I go the same way? We need to develop our capacity to continue to relate to the person with dementia as a real person, with real feelings, not just a dependent non-person needing only physical care. We have to find ways to reinforce the person's humanity, rather than undermine their already precarious sense of self. How we respect and respond to people with dementia influences how they see themselves, which in turn influences how they behave, despite the underlying neurological damage.

Although sooner or later dementia affects all cognitive functions, it is recent memory that is lost first. Recall of more distant times, places and people, especially memories relating to personal life experience (episodic memory) and associated physical skills and actions (procedural memory) may remain relatively intact or partially intact far into the disease. It is possible to key into these early memories to extract their riches, encourage conversation, stimulate activities and, in so doing, preserve sociability.

This is possible even if the person is unable to name the day of the week or to say where they are or what they had for breakfast.

If you want to undertake reminiscence work with people with dementia and their carers, you must set realistic goals, taking account of your own level of expertise, available assistance, access to supervision and the context in which you are working. Considerable sensitivity, empathy, patience and skill are required. The guidance given in earlier chapters is relevant but needs to be substantially modified.

The importance of having clear objectives

In planning to reminisce with people who have dementia and their family and professional carers, it is crucial to be clear about what you hope to achieve and how you intend to proceed. Objectives usually emphasise:

- encouraging sociability and lessening isolation by preserving and developing personal relationships;
- having fun and encouraging communication;
- providing social and intellectual stimulation by exercising retained abilities;
- decreasing boredom by involvement in creative reminiscence-related activities;
- preserving a sense of identity and self-esteem;
- reducing anxiety;
- sustaining family and paid carers, and developing their understanding and skills;
- informing assessments and care plans.

Workers with professional training are also using reminiscence in systematic structured life reviews, counselling and psychotherapy with carefully selected people who have dementia and whose behaviour is troubled and troubling and with people with low mood, depression or unresolved problems.

Supporting carers

Many family and paid carers find dementia care exceedingly stressful, even if rewarding. Without adequate support systems, it may become overwhelming. Mutual involvement in reminiscence makes it easier to concentrate effort on what people can still do, rather than be overwhelmed by what they can no longer do. Because it is a low-risk, easily managed, relatively cheap, enjoyable and effective psychosocial intervention, it also gives carers pleasure and satisfaction. It helps to prevent them from setting the person with dementia up for failure by making unrealistic, stressful demands on their failing short-term memory and other compromised abilities because it principally relies on long-term memory.

Family carers, professional carers and reminiscence workers are often surprised at how well people with mild to moderate dementia can reminisce. Even in later stages when the response seems relatively small and transitory judged by 'ordinary' standards, it can still give great mutual pleasure to the person and the carer and help to hold both in warm, loving relationships.

Communicating with people with dementia

John Killick (2005) catches our habitual failure to connect with people who have dementia:

> *'What have I got to tell them? Stories!*
> *And nobody asks, so I don't bother telling them.'*
> From *Conversation (Journal of Dementia Care* Calendar 2005)

Professional and family carers have to develop ways of communicating that respect the person and reach beyond ordinary speech. Goldsmith (1996) suggests that, despite language and memory problems, it is possible to communicate with people with dementia. It requires great patience, time and empathy – a willingness to try to see the world through their eyes, rather than through your own, to walk in their shoes or sit in their chair (Kitwood 1997). By listening carefully to conversation about the past you can learn to appreciate the person as they used to be and as they are now. An accepting, non-critical attitude and willingness to try are far more important than a list of techniques. Abandon your expectations that people with dementia should be able to converse as they used to if only they would try harder; they have changed and so must you.

Non-verbal communication – reading and responding to body language

Everyone, with or without dementia, uses both words and body language to communicate. When brain damage disrupts verbal language, skill in reading non-verbal body language becomes crucial. *Body language* refers to body movement, facial expression, eye movements, touch, physical appearance, posture, gesture and use of personal space or positioning. *Verbal communication* refers to pitch, intonation and rate of speaking as well as content. In dementia there may be vague and empty speech, diminished or impoverished vocabulary, changes in word association patterns, difficulty in finding words, using incorrect words, repetition and disordered conversation. Whilst it is crucial to listen carefully and try to unravel or decode the meanings of speech and the associated emotions, it is just as important to encourage non-verbal expression and to become skilled in 'reading' this form of communication. Below are some simple tips, which are also relevant to communication with people who have other types of learning, visual, hearing or speech difficulties. Techniques like these can help but only if you have genuine regard and respect for the person with a disability, in this case dementia, who will usually be very perceptive about how you feel towards them. Accurate observation and empathy are the keys to good communication.

Guidelines and suggestions

Setting the scene

- Check the basics. Spectacles need to be clean and of the right prescription, hearing aids properly fitted and functioning, and dentures in place.
- Do not compete with other distractions such as the radio or television; turn them off or move to another room.
- Try to meet in a well-lit room and do not cover your mouth with your hand. Eye contact is always important (provided it is not impolite in the person's culture) when you are either speaking or listening.

- Sit at the same level as the other person.

- Attract the person's attention before you speak, make eye contact, smile and use touch.

- Relax and concentrate your attention so that you are listening attentively. Try to be calm and to remain calm. If you are hurried and tense, there is every possibility that the person will sense your unease.

Worker's interactions

- Take the initiative in beginning a conversation. People find it hard to get started.

- Remain still. Moving around or changing places can distract.

- You may want to link arms and walk together if a person is restless, but talking while walking may not be easy.

- Speak slowly and clearly but never in a childish way. Do not talk down to people and never talk over their heads to someone else.

- Do not try to correct the person. Do not argue. Accept what is said.

- Use touch at times if this seems acceptable.

- Slow down, take time, give the person time to gather their thoughts together and time to respond.

- Use short sentences. If asking questions, these should be simple and direct. Ask only one question at a time. Open-ended questions are usually more productive.

- Try rephrasing if you are not understood, always using low, not high-pitched, tones. Never shout.

- Encourage actions, movement, mime and demonstration.

- Be open to various interpretations. A person might use one word when another is meant.

- Respond to the person's underlying emotions and intended communication, as you understand it, rather than being preoccupied with factual accuracy.

- Use encouraging smiles and head nods. Appear relaxed – taking up a relaxed posture helps you to become relaxed.

- Make good use of humour, as a person's sense of humour often survives dementia.

- Shared pleasure and laughter (and tears), even without words, bring people closer together.

Dawn Brooker, a psychologist, has described communication with people with dementia as 'like a game of tennis, with a message rather than a ball being batted backwards and forwards' (Harris 2005, page 125). The carer's task is to coach, not to win. Pre-match preparation is essential to create the best conditions so as to gain attention, and to learn to lob the ball with the best chance of a successful return so that both players can enjoy what is happening between them.

If you want a person with dementia to undertake a task, analyse it first so it can be broken down into separate small steps. This way there is a better chance of the person being able to perform the task. Give warm praise and encouragement. Never use negative examples or critical responses to reinforce a point, and concentrate on what a person can still do rather than on what they can no longer do.

Reminiscence is only one imaginative means that can be used to lessen the social isolation of older people, especially older people with dementia. Loss of memory does not automatically mean loss of creativity or capacity to feel and to express empathy. Music, movement, mime, touch, dance, drama and art can all be used, or used in conjunction with reminiscence.

Rather than thinking that the seemingly garbled, often repetitive, talk of people with dementia is meaningless, some people are learning to 'read', unravel and respond to the symbolism, metaphor and emotional content of the words used. John Killick (1994, page 16), a poet, listens very attentively to people with dementia and records their conversations, which he crafts into poetry to give back to the person. He explains it in this way:

> *'It seems to me that language used by people with dementia*
> *is a metaphorical one – where what they say often does*
> *not make sense in the usual literal way but has a poetic or*
> *symbolic meaning. People express themselves in language*

nearer to poetry than they used before. For example, one lady talked about her experience as a monkey puzzle, and another expressed a yearning for freedom as riding on a swing.'

Sometimes the conversation refers to the past; sometimes to poignant, insightful comment on the present. Here are two poems from his book *You Are Words: Dementia poems* (pages 10 and 39) that illustrate these points.

'You Are Words'

Life is a bit of a strain,
in view of what is to come.
Sometimes I feel embarrassed
talking to anybody, even you.
You don't really like to burden
other people with your problems.
I have been a strict person.
What people and children do now
is completely different. Any beauty
or grace has been desecrated.
The circle of life is shot away.
I want to thank you for listening.
You see, you are words.
Words can make or break you.
Sometimes people don't listen,
they give you words back,
and they're all broken, patched up.
But will you permit me to say
that you have the stillness of silence,
that listens and lasts.

'Grass'

A young fella carried me
in here; it were a long way
and a long time ago.
I were lying on grass ...
I don't want to stay, no
there's nothing for me
they're all very kind
but I don't want to be
inside anywhere at all
it's much too hot and bright
it just don't feel right
I've not been used
I need the fresh air
I keep calling out;
Nurse, Nurse, carry me
outside to where
I were lying on grass

Special places and spaces that encourage reminiscence

In addition to these creative ways of reaching out to people with dementia, the design of residential and day care facilities can assist or detract from dementia care. Décor and furnishings are sometimes deliberately designed to resemble times past. Mary Marshall (1998) describes internationally accepted principles of design that may apply to an entire facility or sometimes to particular rooms and gardens. These places provide a sympathetic atmosphere in which familiar surroundings stimulate recall. Outdoor spaces, gardens utilising old-fashioned perfumed plants, sociable sitting and activity areas, and safe wandering paths and special reminiscence rooms are increasingly used to provide stimulation, orientation, pleasure and security.

> ***Mary McIlwaine, care worker*** *'I furnished a room in Shankill House as a Belfast kitchen-house. Walking into it with a resident is like walking into their past. We have another room furnished as a pub with old-fashioned beer mats, bottles,*

photos and furniture. In here the men tell many a yarn over a pint of Guinness.'

Develop the habit of thinking systematically about making use of the natural and designed environment to mark different stages of people's life journeys and the places and people that were and possibly still may be important to them. In ever-widening circles embracing a person's bedroom, present home, neighbourhood and community, cherished possessions, significant landmarks and sacred places can be identified and used as way markers, signposts and hooks on which to hang present conversations.

Guidelines for planning dementia-specific reminiscence groups

Deciding whether to do individual work or groupwork will depend upon the persons involved, the context in which you are working and the objectives you wish to achieve. Groupwork with people with dementia is not only possible but is also very rewarding, provided that groups are small – usually with no more than two to four members, who must be selected with great care. Such small groups enable each member actively to participate and to feel that they and their contributions are valued. Remember that many older people with dementia are also likely to have sensory impairments that may hinder participation in a group. Some people will prefer the opportunities for personal, undivided attention that individual work provides.

Many, however, enjoy the sociability of a small group that can counteract the encroaching isolation caused by memory loss and associated language difficulties. In a small intimate group where people feel relaxed and appreciated, they often rediscover the rules of conversation such as turn taking, listening to others and responding warmly to other people's contributions. The gains from meeting in a small group must be balanced with the problem many people with Alzheimer's disease have of keeping track of who said what in a group conversation, so special care is required when selecting potential participants.

In small numbers, people with dementia can also participate successfully in groups where the majority of members do not have obvious memory difficulties. Depending on individual circumstances, they do not always need to be segregated in dementia-specific groups. Successful membership of a heterogeneous group can be stimulating and rewarding, provided that the other members are encouraging and tolerant.

The general advice already given about excluding people with particular kinds of problems from groups also applies to those who have dementia (see Chapter 4). Do not include any person in a group who is likely to harm another member or make it impossible for others to participate comfortably.

Even in a very small group it is helpful to have two leaders in order to give personal attention, to share tasks and to cope if anyone becomes upset or wishes to leave the group. With more helpers, groups can be larger and can effectively use a mixture of paired activities, small group and whole group activities.

Remembering Yesterday, Caring Today projects

Larger groups with up to twenty people have been used very successfully in Remembering Yesterday, Caring Today (RYCT) projects pioneered by the European Reminiscence Network. These time-limited groups consist of people with dementia, their family carers, volunteers and leaders drawn from various health, social care and artistic backgrounds. RYCT groups combine richly varied shared reminiscence activities and parallel psychoeducational training and support for carers. These groups emphasise having fun together, breaking down barriers, learning and re-learning to communicate, enhancing relationships and encouraging sociability. Bruce, Hodgson and Schweitzer's (1999) RYCT handbook – translated into Catalan, Danish, Dutch, French, German, Italian, Spanish and Swedish – gives detailed guidance on how to run RYCT groups and particularly how to manage paired, small group and whole group activities within a session.

Obtaining consent

Obtaining consent is important when seeking to involve people with dementia in reminiscence but is not always easy to achieve. Always extend a brief, honest invitation, supplemented by a simple written explanation.

Encourage people to come, remind them on the day and be finely tuned to non-verbal signs of pleasure or distress. Make it possible for people to indicate in whatever way they are able that they do not wish to participate. With restless people, it is best to leave the door of the meeting room ajar, and do not prevent anyone from leaving if they so wish.

If a person comes, remains and seems to enjoy the experience, their assent may be taken as consent. It is advisable, although not strictly necessary, to obtain the consent of principal relatives and to secure their cooperation whenever possible. Although most welcome the opportunity for involvement, there may be someone who does not wish their family member to undertake reminiscence.

Adapting style, pace and programme

It is recommended that sessions be held more frequently than once a week over several months if possible. They should always be held in the same place, at the same time of day and follow the same general pattern. Some workers like to provide familiarity and a sense of continuity by wearing the same clothes, perfume or after-shave at each session. A regular structure or pattern to the group meeting is desirable. Identical opening and ending rituals, songs, greetings and goodbyes, using mascots, symbols, colours and candles, or simple actions such as joining hands can provide continuity, reminders and a sense of security, inclusion and stability.

Try to hold the group at the time of day when the members are more lucid. Careful observation will reveal what is their best or worst time. As a rough general guide, many people with dementia seem to be more restless and disorientated in the late afternoon or twilight, perhaps because of altered visual cues caused by changing light and deepening shadows. Well-planned reminiscence held at this time of day can constructively occupy 'sundowners' and effectively counteract their anxious preoccupations over lost attachment figures by giving them undivided attention, distraction and reassurance.

A person with dementia cannot be expected to call up specific memories on demand. You have to set the scene and provide the relevant and appropriate stimuli. Sessions may need to be shorter than an hour but many people with mild to moderate dementia can remain interested far longer than is usually expected, provided that the triggers and the topics are relevant. If people become restless, adjust the programme. Switch to triggers that stimulate other senses or introduce another activity to match the mood of the members, which is likely to vary anyway within meetings and from meeting to meeting. Allow time for unhurried refreshments and a physical activity that enables members to act out or transform recalled memories into physical, artistic or other creative formats by means of drama, mime, movement, singing, dance or art.

Multi-sensory triggers are especially important and they should relate closely to people's known background, previous interests and preferred sensory pathways. Do not overwhelm or overload people. Use triggers sparingly and selectively, usually one at a time and in sequence so that all senses can be used as pathways to cognitive, emotional, physical and social stimulation.

It is very natural to combine reminiscing with other activities that depend on procedural long-term memory – memories for actions lodged, as it were, in the muscles and bones of people. Make full use of humour and create opportunities for everyone to enjoy themselves, to be friends and to have a good time together (Schweitzer 1998b).

Montessori methods in dementia care

Interesting parallels have been made between the Montessori approach to educating very young children and rehabilitating people with dementia by means of companionable engagement in long-practised tasks that are retrieved and reconstructed through reminiscence and recall. The following example illustrates this point.

> 'If the Montessori activity is polishing silverware, a daughter might reminisce with her mother about dinners she served or parties they attended together. Working together on a meaningful project can give joy in the moment, and perhaps bring back shared joy from long ago.' (Brenner and Brenner 2004, page 25)

Brenner and Brenner suggest that the Montessori principles on which this approach is based include:

- use of real-life materials that are aesthetically pleasing;
- progression from simple to complex, concrete to abstract;
- materials and procedures structured so that participants can work from left to right, and from top to bottom;
- materials arranged in order from largest to smallest, and from most to least;
- learning progresses in an orderly sequence: participant watches presentation, tries replicating it and talks about the activity;
- activities are broken into component parts, and one component is practised at a time;
- the risk of failure is minimised, and the chances of success are maximised;
- as little vocalisation as possible is used when demonstrating activities;
- participation is always invited and never enforced;
- when presenting activities the speed of movement is slowed to match the speed of the participants;
- wherever possible the materials and activity are made self-correcting;
- whenever possible the participants are encouraged to create something that can be used by the larger community;
- the environment is adapted to the needs of the participants;
- whenever possible the participants select the activities.

With detailed knowledge of a person's background it is easy to see how these principles can incorporate a reminiscence dimension that is well matched to earlier life experience. In this way the Montessori goal of assisting people to become as independent as possible is encouraged.

Locating and using relevant triggers

Speak with older friends, relatives and others with local knowledge so that you can discover what triggers relate to the past life of the people with whom you plan to reminisce. You may be fortunate in being able to use people's own personal possessions. It may be possible to borrow artefacts from places where people once worked or to find volunteers with similar work backgrounds who might join a group. It is an added bonus if the group leaders and volunteers share the same background as members and have a familiar accent or idiom.

> **Day centre worker** *'People with dementia come to our day centre for two days a week. It's in an area of the town where a lot of people live who once worked in the local mill so we have gathered up a lot of old bobbins, spools, wool and different types of cloth. We also have old newspapers with pictures of mills and mill workers, and our local museum gave us a recording of a mill hooter, a sort of siren that was blown at the start and end of the shift. We use all these things with two or three women together, or sometimes just with one person, to get them talking.'*

Communicating through music

Music is especially effective for people with dementia, but like all other interventions it must be used in a person-centred way. David Aldridge (2000), a university teacher and researcher, suggests that music serves many functions, including calming and comforting people who are agitated; reducing wandering; improving self-esteem; stimulating memories and emotions; connecting people; and lifting the spirit. Musical ability seems to be retained long after other abilities have deteriorated. Some people with no evidence of prior musical ability or earlier musical training, given non-threatening opportunities to participate in singing, music making and listening to music, do so with obvious pleasure.

Encourage people to play percussion instruments, sing along, tap their feet, sway, wave scarves, clap or dance. Words or fragments of once-loved songs and hymns may be sung, sometimes spontaneously, sometimes with prompting, even when ordinary speech has deteriorated. Live music evokes rich responses and gives great pleasure. It may also trigger sad recollections. Take the trouble to discover what kind of music each person may have enjoyed and now prefers. Do not expect everyone to share the same tastes, and ask relatives if they can provide previously loved tapes or CDs. Music combined with physical movement or used together with other methods of sensory stimulation has proved effective. Simpler, slower and clearer melodies may come to be appreciated as much as old favourites (Clair 1996).

> **Nurse** *'It was as a student nurse on my first ward that I first looked after an Alzheimer's patient. Mrs Smith was loud and it was impossible to have a conversation with her. She had a tendency to be violent, was agitated and she would not eat or drink.*
>
> *'I started singing to her. At first she did not respond at all, but after a short time she began to join in. Not only did she know the words of all the songs but she had a wonderful singing voice. This woman who could not speak a coherent sentence could sing perfectly.'*

Reminiscing with troubled individuals

If you are caring for particularly troubled and troubling individuals whose behaviour you find challenging, specific reminiscence is worth trying. Neurological damage caused by dementia, past life experience, personality and present circumstances will all be implicated in contributing to disruptive behaviour. Because these troubled people create so many difficulties for everyone around them – including other older people, family carers and paid carers as well as themselves – if you can make life better for them, you make life better for everyone else as well.

The importance of senior staff support

Many group living facilities and day centres do not customarily provide opportunities for intensive attention to individuals although an activity programme based on groupwork may be in place. If specific reminiscence work is to be undertaken that involves giving more time and attention than is customary to a particular person, it is essential for senior staff to include a note in the care plan and carefully explain what is intended to all staff, including administrative, care and domestic staff. Without such official backing from managers, any worker asked to undertake specific reminiscence work with an individual will feel isolated, unsupported and even sabotaged. (Chapter 4 discusses the crucial need for support from senior managers.)

If this support is not given, other staff will criticise their colleague for neglecting ordinary duties and for paying too much attention to one person. The work attempted will be undermined and undone if all staff members have not been persuaded that it is right to single out someone for concentrated personal attention. Work can be sabotaged in many different ways unless all the staff believe that reminiscence and life story work are 'real work', as the following example shows:

> **Research worker** 'Mary was selected for "specific" reminiscence work. She was a most unhappy, isolated, aggressive, anorexic woman who pushed, hit, spat and shouted at anyone who came near. The key worker collected a detailed life history from Mary's niece and discovered that, when younger, Mary had always liked nice things such as fine china, good linen and small delicate flowers.

> 'So the key worker decided to try to tempt her to eat by setting a breakfast tray with a linen tray cloth, special china and a posy of flowers. Mary started to eat better and some days she asked for a second piece of toast. Her aggression decreased and her isolation lessened. On the days when the key worker was off duty, the special arrangements were ignored because the cook refused to set the tray, so opposed was she to the idea of one resident being singled out for special attention. Several weeks passed before the officer in charge confronted the cook and instructed her not to undermine the care plan and to set the tray.'

Observation

Specific work must begin with careful observation over several days. Managers must make it possible for the selected staff member to have time to do this and to write a detailed personal care plan, which will need to be reviewed from time to time. This may mean allocating additional staff time. More often it means using existing staff time differently.

The work is based on careful, precise observation of present behaviour and detailed life history information used to illuminate the present. Observations need to cover the daily pattern of life so as to identify any recurring positive or negative features and to detect any related circumstances or timings. Close observation draws a picture of the person's present lifestyle. It is advisable to observe:

- times of the day or night when the person may be especially happy or unhappy, disturbed, troubled, restless or agitated;
- time spent alone;
- interactions with other residents or staff;
- preferences for how and where the day is spent;
- the relevance, responsiveness and appropriateness of speech and behaviour;
- variations in mood, lucidity, activity and interests;
- behaviour around major routines of the day such as getting up, bedtime, bathing, toileting and meals;
- ability to manage self-care and other activities of daily living;
- personal preferences for food, clothes, company and activities;
- reactions to visits by friends, family or volunteers.

Gathering life history details

Information about life history draws a picture of the person's past lifestyle, which can then be used to help 'decode' the observations of present behaviour. The life history connects people to the present. So many older people with dementia who live in care facilities resemble refugees. They are strangers in strange places, cut off from their past and alienated from the present. Life history, skilfully used, can link a distant past with a problematic present. It enables carers to understand what may be contributing to a person's present behaviour and what might possibly improve it.

If the history depends only on what the person can tell about themselves, the past may remain very shadowy, just a fleeting glimpse. The details of the life history must therefore be collected from all possible sources, including the older person, their relatives, their contemporaries and agency records.

Too frequently these records give only negative accounts of recent or present functioning. They tend to be problem-focused and emphasise physical symptoms. They stress what people can no longer do, and say little about what capacities remain and what interests might be preserved or revived. Imagine your own life to date summarised in just a few lines on an assessment form. This would not do justice to you now at a much younger age. Yet this is often all that is known about the long lives of so many older people in hospitals, care homes or day centres (Bell and Troxel 1997; 2001).

Be sensitive but persistent in researching the life history. Try to pick up clues about significant past events, people and places and possible present resource people. Keep careful records of what you learn. Useful information includes:

- important chronological events such as births, deaths and marriages;
- information about parents;
- childhood, school and student days;
- spouses, partners, children, grandchildren;
- family life and work;
- significant friends and relationships;
- significant pets and possessions;
- major life crises or trauma, landmarks, changes or branching points and transitions;
- where World War II was spent and how it was experienced;
- places lived in or visited;
- hobbies, interests, trips and preferred music and recreation.

Start reminiscing with the person. Learn to listen very attentively and respond to the expressed emotions. Conversation may need to be decoded or translated. Listen for recurring themes or repeated words. Do not be preoccupied with establishing factual accuracy. Try to decipher the symbolic meanings and unravel the metaphors. If you begin by assuming truth rather than falsity, belief rather than disbelief, genuineness not confabulation, much valuable information can be gathered.

Stop labelling people as 'confused' and dismissing muddled conversation as irrelevant, especially if a person is obviously upset, perhaps struggling to tell you about something that has caused them hurt in either the distant or the recent past. Try to get sufficient clues to check the story out with someone who may remember something from the past that has now 'leaked' into the present.

Too often when a person with dementia is upset, tearful or distressed about a past memory that has intruded into the present, workers hastily change the conversation, attempt distraction or denial. Some may even physically or emotionally remove themselves from the conversation. Try to extend your ability to feel your way into the world of the other person. Be more willing to explore past pain and share past sadness. You may be able to piece together the fragments of the story (possibly illuminated by the life history you have gathered) that is causing distress at the present time. The following example of Andy illustrates the need for this kind of detective work.

> **Social worker** *'Andy, who used to be a sociable friendly man, had early-onset dementia. He had withdrawn into a world of silence, no longer even talking to his devoted wife who was determined to care for him at home. During a planned reminiscence session with him at a day centre when a collection of family photographs was being used to try to stimulate conversation, he was shown a picture of Niagara Falls. He launched at once into a long, apparently garbled, tale about a woman who had thrown her baby over the Falls. The worker, thinking this was a bizarre fantasy, hastily changed the conversation. Later, when checking back with his wife, every detail as told by Andy was found to be correct.'*

Involving spouses and partners in reminiscence work

Older relatives, especially spouses and partners, are often delighted to be asked for information. They feel that they are contributing to the care of their loved one who, as the dementia progresses, is almost inevitably becoming a stranger. Positive benefits for the partner from this type of parallel reminiscence can also occur.

Yukiko Kurokawa (1998), a psychologist, describes ways of undertaking shared reminiscence work with couples when one has dementia. She facilitates a simultaneous joint life review, in which couples are helped to recall, share and review memories and integrate their shared life experience. She suggests that by this process the well spouse or partner is better able to cope with the partner's deterioration and both partners enjoy reliving and integrating satisfying aspects of their past lives. This mutual journey is often given tangible form by creating a collage from personal photographs or, if these are unavailable, using pictures from magazines chosen by the participants to capture mood as well as memories.

Making a plan

When the detailed life history has been gathered, make a written plan of how the information is to be used. The plan is only a guide to a possible journey you and the person with whom you are working will take together. There will be unexpected detours, surprises, excitement, shared pleasure and, no doubt, some disappointments as well. You are beginning a demanding journey because you have to be finely tuned to the present as well as to past history. It is essential not to lose sight of physical and emotional care needs related to the person's present care and well-being while being absorbed in gathering the life history details.

Implementing the plan

Use the life history to introduce focused conversation. Discuss cherished memorabilia, perhaps work on a life story book, go on trips, outings or visits to once-significant places, re-introduce old hobbies or follow up old interests to rekindle further recall. The information you have collected will give clues to possible fruitful topics of conversation and enjoyable activities. You become an active proxy memory bank, holding the long-deposited memories on behalf of the person with dementia, drawing on these riches to benefit the owner who requires assistance to access them in the present.

When the conversation is set in safe territory, people may be secure enough to risk responding. Ease them gently into situations and to conversations and activities that emphasise remaining competence, not incompetence. They may be well aware of their deficiencies and need warm loving encouragement, time and patience to risk responding.

Use life history to select triggers and arrange situations that resemble past experience. Helping with the cooking, cleaning or laundry, trips to the seaside or parks and garden centres, a night at the greyhounds, a soccer match or an evening in the local pub can give immense pleasure to people with dementia. They can often 'pass' themselves in such situations without their dementia becoming apparent or inhibiting. Social circumstances and surroundings, if sufficiently familiar, can stir long-dormant memories and well-learned behaviour. The experience is enjoyed at the time but it also provides a focus for future recall, further conversation and recurring satisfaction.

Reviewing the work undertaken

Always take stock of what you have attempted. Give yourself credit for success and face up to failures. Such intensive work with individuals contributes to your own personal and professional development. It helps you to learn that each person, including yourself, is unique and has distinct needs. It helps you understand how the past influences the present. It brings great personal pleasure and increased job satisfaction when you see evidence of your own developing skills and deeper understanding that have improved life for an individual and for others around them.

You find that you can cope better with troubled and troubling people, decreasing their isolation and lessening their unhappiness. Because this kind of individual work changes relationships and decreases the distance between staff and older people, attitudes change, tolerance grows and sympathies are enlarged. You learn to be less frightened and less overwhelmed by the awfulness of dementia.

Officer in charge of a dementia-specific care home
'Elizabeth always disrupted mealtimes by shouting and messing with her food. Her detailed life history showed she had always preferred to lie in and rise late. Instead, our

staff members were getting her up early, hurrying her to get dressed and to come downstairs for breakfast.

'We decided to be more relaxed. She was left to sleep until she woke. Her key worker then helped her to dress at her own pace. By the time she came downstairs, most people had finished breakfast and she could eat in solitude, which seemed to suit her much better. Her shouting disappeared, she complained less about a sore back and she ceased to be a trouble to everyone else.'

Disturbed reactions

Very occasionally, someone may have an over-reaction that is inappropriate to his or her present circumstances. This 'catastrophic reaction' is like an electrical circuit becoming overloaded and an appliance blowing a fuse to avoid further damage. If this happens, try to stay calm; do not waste energy on trying to reason with the distressed person or talk them out of their exaggerated response. Gentle distraction and patience are more likely to be effective. Try to keep life simple with gentle routines that provide order without rigidity, security without monotony. Do not take the upset personally but think about whether something that you did or current circumstances might have innocently provoked the unforeseen exaggerated outburst.

If something in a reminiscence session seemed to trigger the eruption, avoid those particular triggers, topics or associations in future sessions. The behaviour may be totally unrelated to your reminiscence work, so do not hastily conclude that reminiscence has caused the distress.

Reminiscence, reality orientation, cognitive rehabilitation and validation therapy

Reality orientation, cognitive rehabilitation and validation therapy are used with people with dementia (Woods et al 2005). Reminiscence work is used, regardless of whether or not participants have dementia, although it requires adaptation when used with people with dementing conditions.

Sometimes reminiscence and reality orientation are talked about as if they were identical, because some aspects resemble each other. They are, however, very different in their underlying theoretical ideas and values. Cognitive rehabilitation is used with people who have many kinds of neurological impairments, not only those caused by dementia (Clare et al 2003). Validation therapy, although based on different assumptions, has more in common with reminiscence work, as it too values a person's past and seeks to understand whatever from the past seems to preoccupy the older person with advanced dementia in the present.

Reality orientation and cognitive rehabilitation

Taulbee and Folson (1966) first described reality orientation (RO) with older hospitalised psychiatric patients as a way of affirming their uniqueness and humanity and improving their quality of life. It developed as a method for helping older people beset by failing memory to remain in touch with the present. This was attempted in two ways. The first used special classes or group activities that emphasised the here and now. The second, known as 24-hour reality orientation, was implemented through consistent behaviour by all staff and the provision of reminders or memory joggers within the total care environment. These reminders included notice boards, calendars, large clocks, and colour coding and labelling of doors.

Earlier enthusiasm for group reality orientation has largely disappeared because it was time-consuming, relatively ineffective, disregarded the time orientation and emotional preoccupations of people with dementia and imposed the values, time perspectives and priorities of staff. It was frequently confrontational and tended to focus on lost rather than retained abilities. Its emphasis, however, on colour coding, labelling and signage has constructively influenced ideas about the design of contemporary dementia facilities.

Over recent years more sensitive techniques have evolved out of reality orientation. The emphasis now involves a more holistic approach that is responsive to the emotional, behavioural and cognitive needs of individuals and their carers. These developments include cognitive stimulation, retraining and cognitive rehabilitation programmes that are designed to overcome specific memory problems of immediate concern to individuals with early-stage dementia and their carers (Spector et al 1998; Clare 2005).

Cognitive rehabilitation pays attention to emotional as well as cognitive needs and the impact of dementia on families; it seeks to develop collaborative strategies for coping with memory difficulties and other cognitive changes. Memory aids such as diaries, notes and reminders, simple intensive learning techniques, technical devices and environmental modification are used to assist people with early-stage dementia to cope with specific everyday problems. They are helped to achieve clearly defined specific outcomes that seek to improve their functioning and well-being (Clare et al 2003).

Validation therapy

The goals of validation therapy are to:

- restore a feeling of self-worth;
- reduce stress;
- justify living;
- work towards resolving unfinished conflicts from the past;
- increase verbal and non-verbal communication;
- improve gait and physical well-being;
- prevent withdrawal;
- reduce the need for chemical and physical restraints (de Klerk-Rubin 1994).

Validation therapy is used with much older people with advanced dementia who are deeply disturbed by the resurgence of memories of loss, trauma or grief associated with events in their past lives. Reality as perceived by the person in the here and now is respected. No attempt is made to dissuade people of their erroneous views; for example, that they must get home because their mother is waiting for them or their own children need their tea prepared. Instead the therapist listens to the words being used and the concerns being expressed. The therapist empathises with the expressed emotional needs of the person and interprets the feelings behind the words. Feil (2002) suggests that this disturbed behaviour represents the struggle of the person with dementia to revert to a more secure past as a means of surviving an all too desolate present. Validation therapy may be undertaken with individuals and with groups. De Klerk-Rubin (1994; 1995) describes both individual and group approaches, and the role of the validation therapist.

Reminiscence and validation therapy share the assumptions that an interest in the past life of older people is important for its own sake, not just as a means of keeping them in touch with present reality, and that it is important to validate or affirm the feelings associated with that past. Both respect the past and use it to help the older person retain a sense of identity, personhood and emotional security in the present.

Conclusion

Reminiscence and related creative activities, especially music and those that stimulate body movements such as drama and mime, which stress non-verbal communication, have much to contribute to people with various kinds of dementia. Reminding carers of significant shared life experience can lessen their isolation and desperation and help reassure the people with dementia that they can still communicate and share a trusting, loving relationship. In doing dementia-specific reminiscence work with troubled and troubling people, detailed knowledge of each person's life history supplemented by careful observation are invaluable tools for working with them in the present. Creativity, imagination, willingness to experiment and capacity for valuing and enjoying the moment are central to working effectively with people who have dementia.

KEY POINTS

- Communicating with people with dementia is possible but takes time and skill.

- Reminiscence work requires adaptation for people with dementia.

- Reminiscence work is more effective if done in very small groups or with individuals and couples.

- Reminiscence and linked creative activities provide constructive roles for paid and family carers and volunteers.

- Knowing a person's life story and using it in the present helps achieve person-centred care. It assists the retention of a sense of identity and holds people in relationship with others.

- The key to successful work is to appreciate the individual – as he or she used to be and now is.

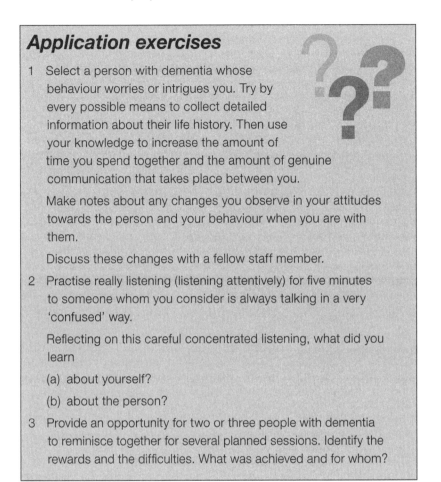

Application exercises

1   Select a person with dementia whose behaviour worries or intrigues you. Try by every possible means to collect detailed information about their life history. Then use your knowledge to increase the amount of time you spend together and the amount of genuine communication that takes place between you.

    Make notes about any changes you observe in your attitudes towards the person and your behaviour when you are with them.

    Discuss these changes with a fellow staff member.

2   Practise really listening (listening attentively) for five minutes to someone whom you consider is always talking in a very 'confused' way.

    Reflecting on this careful concentrated listening, what did you learn

    (a) about yourself?

    (b) about the person?

3   Provide an opportunity for two or three people with dementia to reminisce together for several planned sessions. Identify the rewards and the difficulties. What was achieved and for whom?

Further reading

Bender M. (2005) *Therapeutic Groupwork for People with Cognitive Losses: Working with people with dementia.* Bicester: Speechmark

Bruce E, Hodgson S and Schweitzer P. (1999) *Reminiscing with People with Dementia: A handbook for carers.* London: Age Exchange

Killick J and Allan K. (2001) *Communication and the Care of People with Dementia.* Buckingham: Open University Press

Marshall M. (1997) *State of the Art in Dementia Care.* London: Centre for Policy on Ageing

11 Reminiscence with people who are depressed

Learning outcomes

After studying this chapter you should be able to:

- recognise the impact of loss in later life
- identify whether to undertake group or individual reminiscence work with people who are depressed
- appreciate the importance of using cherished objects in reminiscence work
- outline the key components of a structured life review

Loss in later life

Depression, a disorder of mood, is the biggest threat to mental health and well-being in old age. Various biological, psychological and social factors interact to predispose, precipitate and perpetuate depression. In later life, depression may continue to affect people who have experienced earlier recurring depressive episodes or have long grappled with the mood swings associated with bipolar disorder or manic–depressive illness. Depression may become apparent only in mid or later life as relationships and circumstances change or earlier unresolved problems re-emerge. It may be mistaken for a dementing illness, or occur simultaneously with dementia. Depression in older people too frequently goes unrecognised, unassessed and unassisted. Because much depression responds to treatment, such neglect, whether arising from ignorance or indifference, is unacceptable.

Depression is frequently associated with the experience of loss. Loss is universal and inevitable as people grow older. It comes in many forms and challenges people's ability to cope with and to enjoy life. It is not just loss of loved ones, a partner, husband or wife, siblings, friends, adult children or grandchildren. A sense of coherence, which enables us to believe in a world that is comprehensible, manageable and meaningful, may begin to fragment. Physical health and vigour, perhaps mental capacity as well, may decline. The roles and responsibilities once undertaken with competence and satisfaction dwindle or disappear. Many people are obliged to move home, to scale down, to shed belongings. They experience the loss of special people, familiar places, cherished possessions, gardens, pets and pastimes that were once significant.

It is impossible to understand the processes of ageing without understanding loss, grief and bereavement but there can also be gains, development, growth and satisfaction in later life. New relationships may blossom and new interests be acquired. Grandchildren bring pleasure and a sense of continuity. Loss and relinquishment, however, remain as recurring, often dominating, experiences for many older people. Associated feelings of anger, grief, guilt, longing, numbness, pain, shock and loneliness are common. (See also Chapter 14.)

Following the loss of a long-time spouse or partner, both emotional and practical needs are considerable. Feelings of loss are frequently accompanied by deep anxieties about coping in the immediate present, and the future may look very threatening. Throughout a long-time partnership, most couples divide up different roles and responsibilities. When one partner dies, moves to a care home or develops an incapacitating illness, the other person will be faced with having to take on new tasks and responsibilities.

Apprehension can be decreased and confidence restored if the surviving spouse or partner can be helped to recognise and rediscover through reminiscence and recall how they coped with various difficulties at earlier stages of life. This can lead them to recover, revive, rehearse and re-learn old ways of coping. New learning also occurs while enduring loss and grief. Emotional support and practical coping go hand in hand if earlier but abandoned skills are to contribute to surviving and surmounting loss and bereavement.

Faced with needing to acquire new skills and ways of coping, reminiscence is often used by people of all ages to help solve present problems. The need to confront any stressful event is likely to precipitate a tendency to reminisce. In crisis situations, reminiscence will be a particularly relevant and common response that discerning workers or family carers can use to help the stressed person to cope.

The impact of the loss and how it affects the person's own sense of self and other relationships become important aspects of the mourning process. Recalling past coping can make present problems less frightening and also provide reassurance about future coping (Cappeliez 2002). Reminiscence encourages people to value past competence and earlier achievements and hence to value themselves, even if the present is distressing and the future threatening. Not all reminiscence, however, is constructive. If old problems are revived without associated memories of how difficulties were overcome, a person's confidence and optimism are likely to be further undermined (Cappeliez, O'Rourke and Chaudhury 2005). For depressed people who achieve a constructive reappraisal of the past and who manage to integrate a new understanding of their own self-worth, reminiscence will have been helpful.

When faced with loss, especially loss of someone very close, people are usually bewildered. The world as they knew it has changed. They find it hard to make sense of what is happening, to feel any optimism about the future or to see the new directions that must be charted. Gradually some measure of acceptance, hope, energy and willingness to invest in new experiences begins to emerge. There are great individual differences in the time it takes people to adjust to their loss, in how they cope and in the means they use to do so. Some develop a succession of illnesses as if unexpressed painful emotions are converted into physical symptoms. Some retreat into depression whilst others who have an active spiritual life, a sense of coherence or a satisfying explanation about the meaning of life seem to cope much better (MacKinlay 2001). Some find unexpected comfort in being reminded of the past, as did this recently bereaved wife who had been married for over 60 years.

> *'I have recovered D— as the man I married – radical, energetic and sociable. The obituary in the* Irish Times *described him as the man I fell in love with and married, not as he became in the last years of his life – apathetic, depressed and withdrawn. His death has given him back to me, not taken him away.*

Finding meaning in life in the face of death

Various writers cited in Watt and Cappeliez (1995) and Hunt, Marshall and Rowlings (1997) suggest that, when advancing age brings the realisation that death is no longer far off but near at hand, people may become self-absorbed, sad or angry as old unresolved conflicts resurface. Experiencing this urge to review one's life, although common, is not universal. It may bring unresolved conflicts or 'unfinished business' to the surface and these sad memories may trigger serious depression or despair. Perhaps it is not so much old age as enforced retirement, at any age, or other earlier major life crisis that triggers this process of spontaneous life review. By the time people reach their 70s or 80s they possibly have less 'unfinished business' to attend to and their life reviews have already been largely completed.

Many older people seem to be demoralised, if not clinically depressed. Cumulative loss and bereavement, or unresolved or incomplete grieving from earlier losses, may lead to a state of chronic or permanent sadness. As people age, they scarcely have time to recover from one loss before they are confronted with another. When losses come thick and fast with little recovery time in between, people may feel chronically sad, overwhelmed and unable or unwilling to invest much energy in fresh beginnings. They and their families may need encouragement to talk together about the past and the present, to value afresh, or perhaps for the first time, achievements and joys, and to understand what life has meant at earlier stages of the life cycle and what it means now.

Depression as a response to dementia

Substantial numbers of people in the early stages of a dementing illness may be very well aware that they are losing their cognitive abilities and that their memory, independence, confidence and competence are being eroded. This can make them fearful, anxious, depressed, even terrified (Cheston and Bender 1999). Both at this stage and later in their dementing illness, some troubled people are well able to benefit from opportunities to discuss their life's journey and to reconsider and resolve or partially resolve past problems. (See also Chapters 10 and 14.)

Depression as a response to admission to care

Living in care homes and hospitals may be sufficient in itself to trigger deep regret, demoralisation or depression. The circumstances that led to the person entering care, rather than the care environment and care experience, may possibly hold the key to some residents' depression.

Regretting their inability to live independently, perhaps older people in care are more likely to complain, to make unfavourable comparisons between their present and past circumstances, and to retreat into negative repetitive reminiscence. They may use reminiscence as a way of preventing themselves from investing in the present unless special efforts are made to help them to come to terms with their changed life circumstances.

Responses to structured life review

Individual structured life review seems to improve people's level of functioning and contentment, as demonstrated in a number of studies. For example, Haight, Michel and Hendrix (2000) followed 256 mentally alert Americans who were admitted to nursing homes over a five-year period. Half were randomly assigned to undertake a structured life review (see Chapter 6) while the other half received their usual care and a friendly visit from a researcher. The two groups were tested on admission, and then re-tested at eight weeks, one year, two years and three years. Fifty-two residents survived three years. Results showed significant persistent improvements over time for the life review group on measures of depression, life satisfaction and self-esteem.

A similar but short-term small pilot controlled study of 30 people diagnosed with dementia who lived in four care homes, a dementia-specific housing with care facility and a care home (nursing) in Northern Ireland demonstrated significant differences between those who undertook a structured life review and made a life story book and the control group who received only their usual care over an eight-week period. Using a pre-test and post-test methodology, scores on measures of cognitive functioning, depression, communication and mood showed significant improvements (Haight and Gibson 2006).

Intractable mental health problems

It is unlikely that life-long mental health problems will diminish with advancing age. Some depressed people who are inclined to be obsessional become preoccupied with looking back, but their guilt and bitterness remain undiminished despite repeated telling of the same story. They may become stuck over one particular episode or period and be unable to move beyond it. They may use reminiscence, as Webster (1997) suggests, for 'bitterness revival', to 'keep memories of old hurts fresh'. Others may have struggled hard to reach some acceptance of their lives and they may have buried painful experiences that are now beyond conscious recall.

Some severely depressed people are so very unhappy and so absorbed in their present distress that they are unable to reminisce. They have neither the energy nor the interest to recall the past. Their self-esteem and life satisfaction may be so precarious that they do not wish to risk re-examining and re-interpreting their past. Butler (1963) suggests that older people who are unable to complete a successful life review become increasingly depressed and despairing in old age. Working with such people requires skilled professional training and is more complex than most reminiscence work.

Inexperienced reminiscence workers are often afraid they will stumble into painful aspects of a person's life and do more harm than good. It is as well to be aware of this possibility but do not let this anxiety prevent you from beginning reminiscence work. The greater risk is in doing nothing, in leaving older, isolated, unhappy people unstimulated and unsupported. Provided that you are empathetic, genuine and responsive and have time for listening, you are unlikely to do harm. Do take notice, though, of what has been said about the need for supervision.

Very occasionally, an older person may experience such painful recall and such deep distress triggered by participating in reminiscence that more skilled help will be required. If this happens, seek advice urgently from senior staff, who will know how to get assistance from appropriate clinical professionals in health and social service agencies.

Choosing group or individual reminiscence work

Reminiscence with people who are depressed must therefore be undertaken with great care. Present depression is likely to influence the content of recalled memories. Depressed people tend to recall depressed memories, so it is important to avoid jumping to the conclusion that their entire life has been sad or unsatisfactory or that they have always been depressed. It may be easier for depressed people to respond to individual work, where they may feel freer to reveal intimate details or talk about parts of their past life that have caused them pain. In these circumstances, individual work is more likely to foster a close, confiding relationship between the older person and the reminiscence worker.

In a group, however, the depressed person, provided that they have sufficient energy to participate and do not feel out of place, may well find their peers to be supportive and constructively reassuring. Group members may challenge habitual negative interpretations and may be able effectively to confront the depressed person with contrary evidence that challenges their negativity and encourages the construction of more positive perceptions. A group also offers the possibility of making new friends. This may be particularly so if people discover the shared experience of painful loss and transitions. Older people know more than younger people about coping with hurt, grief and loss. Pain shared in a warm accepting group may be healed or at least reduced.

In responding to depression, efforts to impart a feeling of independence, confidence and control are very important. Reminiscence can be used as a means of restoring some control to the person, who may at the very least be helped to control the process of recalling, and perhaps recording, in one way or another, their own life story.

Bohlmeijer, Smit and Cuijpers (2003), after reviewing a number of controlled studies, reported that reminiscence and life review as remedies for depression in older people were just as effective as established drug and psychological treatments. Woods (2004), in commenting on this analysis, cautioned that the process by which reminiscence assists in lifting depressed mood remains unclear and requires further research. He also points out that life review, which emphasises evaluation and resolution of past conflicts, achieved no better results than unstructured reminiscence. A possible explanation, he suggests, was the inclusion of both group and individual life review studies in the review. Like Haight, Coleman and Lord (1995), Woods suggests that life review is best undertaken with individuals.

If the reminiscence or life review process seems unhelpful for an individual, alternative assistance should be considered. For some people it may be helpful to combine these approaches with pharmacological treatments rather than to choose one or the other. It should also be remembered that telling one's story may not always be healing – for some people it may lead to further self-preoccupation or disabling introspection (see Chapter 3). Professional counselling of various types, psychotherapy, cognitive behaviour therapy or approaches that rely more on non-verbal communication such as art, dance or music therapies may be more effective.

As people approach death, some may be fearful, others hopeful. People's attitudes towards death are very likely to be influenced by the culture and religion in which they have been raised. Some may use reminiscence for the purpose of death preparation while others, for example some Orthodox Jews, may prefer not to talk openly about death as they are enjoined to maintain hope at all costs. As they approach death, people who lack a sense of personal continuity, for whatever reason, may experience a sense of profound regret, of opportunities missed, of chances forgone, of paths not taken, and they may feel cheated or short-changed. Not everyone is able to find a satisfying explanation for the meaning of life in general or their own life in particular that assists them to face death with peace of mind (see Chapter 14).

Tangible records

For people who have always invested much of themselves in their work, some written or pictorial account of their life may provide reassurance. Tangible evidence that life has been worthwhile or, if not worthwhile, at least not in vain, may bring reassurance. Placing themselves visually in the context of their wider family through researching and drawing a family tree sometimes helps people achieve a sense of self-acceptance, coherence, continuity and resolution.

Autobiographical writing, including guided group autobiographical writing, and spiritual autobiographies help to develop new perspectives. Elford and colleagues (2005) report encouraging outcomes from an exploratory study of solitary reminiscence writing prompted by photographs and set headings. Seeking forgiveness, reconciliation and making reparation may be stimulated by engagement in writing. Also visits, pilgrimages, family reunions and writing to people who have links or connections with the past have all proved helpful when encouraged within supportive caring relationships. Greater peace of mind and improved quality of life have also been reported as associated outcomes. (See also Chapter 6 for additional suggestions.)

Looking back and looking forward embrace emotional, social and practical dimensions. Working on a life story book, organising and documenting the family photographs, undertaking a structured life review, joining a writing group, creating a collage, making a storyboard, dispersing cherished possessions to people who are personally significant, making a will, assigning enduring power of attorney and writing an advance directive are tangible ways in which people can be helped to evaluate and order their lives.

Using cherished objects in reminiscence

'Memorabilia' refers to things or objects that stir recollection. Sherman (1991) suggests that people who have no access to cherished objects experience a much lower mood and reduced life satisfaction compared with others in similar circumstances who have ready access to cherished objects.

For everyone, depressed or not, cherished possessions provide a sense of historical continuity, comfort and a sense of attachment or belonging. For people who have moved from familiar to unfamiliar surroundings, such objects may be very important because they give a feeling of ownership, continuity and control, and perceived control is known to be influential in creating a sense of well-being (Perrin and May 2000).

Treasured objects also provide opportunities to reminisce and they often seem to have a greater significance for women than for men. They can provide a focus for individual or group reminiscence. For example, residents in a care home could be invited to bring a special object to a session and to talk about its significance. Any attempt to use personal possessions for group reminiscence must be sensitive to the members who have none available and may be mourning their loss.

People who have fled oppression may have few if any cherished objects, photographs or memorabilia of any significance. Their sense of loss may be intensified by the absence of tangible personal reminders that might otherwise have helped them to retain and recall memories of their past life.

If a reminiscence session is to be based on personal memorabilia, it is preferable if all members are able to bring something, no matter how seemingly trivial or commonplace. If this is not possible, they could be asked to describe, or perhaps draw, an object that has significance for them even though it is no longer accessible. Reminiscence work undertaken in a person's own home has limitless opportunities for using ready-to-hand memorabilia.

It is regrettable that so many people admitted to care homes neither bring with them nor retain access to cherished objects. Staff concerned with assessment, admission and care management must take responsibility for ensuring that people entering care homes and special housing bring cherished possessions with them. Older people, family members, housing managers and professional carers may need to be helped to understand the therapeutic importance of cherished objects and other kinds of memorabilia. They may need encouragement to ensure that both men and women coming into care are not bereft of personally significant and familiar artefacts.

Conclusion

Depression in late life too often goes unrecognised and untreated. If combined with dementia, loneliness, low mood, isolation, despair and troubling behaviour are almost inevitable consequences. Knowledge of each person's life history will help you to understand current behaviour and provide clues and cues for how you might try to reach the person in the present. Individual reminiscence and structured life reviews are promising ways of offering assistance and building relationships, and small group reminiscence may help to alter negative self-assessments and open up new friendships. Tangible reminders in the form of cherished objects and other memorabilia can provide a bridge between the past and the present and become a focus for present interactions.

KEY POINTS

- It is important to understand about depression, grief and loss in later life.

- People need to be encouraged to express their disappointments as well as to value their achievements.

- A combination of talking, reflection, life review and production of a tangible record may be more fruitful than simply talking.

- People who are depressed usually recall depressed memories.

- Encourage the recall of episodes of past coping and problem-solving to use as a resource for present coping.

- Seeking reconciliation and making restitution becomes an urgent task for some older people.

- Older people and their families should be encouraged to retain and to use cherished objects to enrich the present.

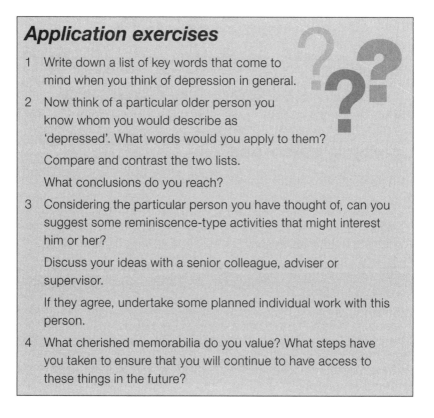

Application exercises

1 Write down a list of key words that come to mind when you think of depression in general.

2 Now think of a particular older person you know whom you would describe as 'depressed'. What words would you apply to them?

   Compare and contrast the two lists.

   What conclusions do you reach?

3 Considering the particular person you have thought of, can you suggest some reminiscence-type activities that might interest him or her?

   Discuss your ideas with a senior colleague, adviser or supervisor.

   If they agree, undertake some planned individual work with this person.

4 What cherished memorabilia do you value? What steps have you taken to ensure that you will continue to have access to these things in the future?

Further reading

Fleming R (Ed). (2001) *Challenge Depression: A manual to help staff identify and reduce depression in aged care facilities.* Canberra: Commonwealth Department of Health and Ageing

Godfrey M and Denby T. (2005) *Depression and Older People.* Bristol: Policy Press

Hunt L, Marshall M and Rowlings C (Eds). (1997) *Past Trauma in Late Life.* London: Jessica Kingsley

Manthorpe J and Iliffe S. (2005) *Depression in Later Life.* London: Jessica Kingsley

12 Reminiscence with people with hearing, sight and speech disabilities

Learning outcomes

After studying this chapter you should be able to:

- appreciate the impact and implications of hearing, sight and speech problems and multiple impairments
- understand the importance of careful assessment, information and advice
- create opportunities for people who have sensory impairments to reminisce
- adapt or modify reminiscence techniques appropriately

The impact of sensory and speech impairments

There are older people with life-long sensory and speech disabilities as well as large numbers of people who develop hearing and sight problems as they grow older. Many people who have a stroke are left with impaired speech and some will also develop dementia. Frequently, ageing people will have more than one disability or impairment. People are described as deafblind if their combined sight and hearing impairments cause difficulties with mobility, communicating and accessing information. Multiple impairments greatly increase the likelihood of the person affected becoming socially isolated as well as having difficulty in carrying out the ordinary tasks of daily living. Sarah J Butler's book *Hearing and Sight Loss* (2004) is an excellent source of comprehensive information about sensory disabilities.

No single sensory or multiple impairment as such should automatically prevent a person from taking part in reminiscence. Provided that proper assessment and care are taken, involvement in reminiscence can lessen social isolation, restore a sense of self-worth, increase confidence and assist in improving a person's quality of life. Too frequently, increasing age combined with one or more communication problems can leave people intensely lonely and isolated, even if they are living surrounded by others, either in a family or in a care facility.

Creating opportunities for participation

Careful assessment of each individual is needed if you are suggesting reminiscence. Consider the person's own wishes and preferences, and work out together, possibly in conjunction with relatives, care staff or a specialist worker, how best to enable each interested person to take part.

Many people who develop sensory disabilities in later life become acutely sensitive to their changed competence. They may also deny their difficulties or be self-conscious about using aids and they may have a higher risk of depression. Multiple sensory problems may be further complicated by dementia. People often report feeling stigmatised or ignored and find that other people stop trying to communicate with them. Misunderstanding or lack of effort by friends, families and professionals can thoughtlessly add to this sense of isolation and loss of confidence. Inadequate or untimely information and absence of suitable aids and adaptations can exacerbate the difficulties.

The more limited a person's ability to communicate, the more effective individual work, rather than groupwork, is likely to be. This is only a general working principle because many people with sensory problems can and do manage to participate successfully in small groups. The presence of multiple sensory disabilities, with the possible addition of dementia, however, will add complexity to all reminiscence work with individuals, couples and small groups.

There are really three parties to any decision about whether a person with a serious sensory impairment should join a group. First, the person with the disability must be consulted. Explain carefully what is proposed. Make sure the person has understood. Second, the leader needs to decide whether or not he or she is sufficiently competent to cope. It may also be important to seek advice from specialist staff and if possible to seek out a co-leader with specialist knowledge of specific disabilities.

Third, other potential group members may need to be consulted because special demands will be made of them.

Too often, family members and professional carers make decisions on behalf of older people, especially those with sensory, speech and cognitive disabilities, and presume to speak for them instead of letting them speak for themselves. Be sensitive to attitudes and actions by staff that restrict opportunities and exclude people from activities that they could enjoy.

The following example from a care home shows how the Officer in Charge thought she knew what was best for people when she advised the reminiscence worker:

> *'Don't bother including Mr Brown. Since his stroke he is very hard to understand and he will not be able to join in.'*

The worker persisted and included Mr Brown in a small group. Later he reported:

> *'Mr Brown was very slow to join in at first. Then I handed him the horseshoe and he became very excited and was determined to speak. He responded to everything and people were very patient listening to him.'*

If a potential group member is uncertain about whether to join a group, encourage them to come once or twice to try it out, to see how well they can manage, before making up their minds. Building self-confidence and reducing self-consciousness are very important aspects of working with people who have a disability.

Adapting reminiscence

It will be especially necessary to plan carefully and to adjust the size and seating arrangements of a group, where it meets, how it is run and what trigger materials are used to make it possible for members with sensory problems to benefit.

If a group has a mixed membership that includes some people with a disability, its size and make-up need very careful thought. Small groups with a co-leader or helper are likely to work best. Take care to ensure helpful seating arrangements and good lighting. Usually a small circle is the best arrangement. Use clear, well-modulated speech. The leader or co-leader should sit near the person with the disability and assist him or her to participate in various ways. Reminiscence groups provide many opportunities for members to help each other.

Homogeneous groups consisting of members with similar disabilities are more manageable than a heterogeneous group of people with various disabilities where it is hard to attend to everyone's different needs. If the group consists of some members with a disability and others with none, probably no more than two people with disabilities should be included.

The dual requirements to attend simultaneously to the group and to all the individuals within it are even more demanding if some members have a communication disability. Inexperienced leaders may find themselves initially either ignoring the needs of a single member or, alternatively, paying them so much attention that the needs of the group are ignored. So much goes on, even in a very small group, that it is difficult to be aware of everything, let alone respond appropriately. Honest feedback between co-leaders as well as discussion with a supervisor or consultant is very important in developing self-awareness and a capacity to respond effectively to people who have sensory or speech disabilities.

Multi-sensory triggers can help stimulate discussion and assist everyone, despite their disability, to participate. If people are unable to respond to one kind of trigger, another type may prove effective, so experiment to find a person's preferred and most responsive sensory pathway and how it may best be exploited.

Breaking the ice

Lack of confidence and poor motivation are the first obstacles to surmount when trying to involve people in reminiscence, and low self-esteem and self-consciousness or embarrassment may hinder participation and enjoyment. People with a disability fear making fools of themselves or being a burden to others. This means that you may have to work especially hard at the beginning phase of each session to help people with hearing, speech and visual problems to feel comfortable, secure and relaxed. It may be helpful to begin each session with an exercise that relies on touch and demonstration or mime rather than on hearing, sight or speech.

Here is an example of such an exercise. Hide some relevant small triggers in a box or a bag (at least one for each person present). Pass the bag around so that each person in turn can select a trigger by feel, and then ask them to demonstrate its use to the group, perhaps using mime rather than speech to do so.

This exercise usually produces instant interest, laughter and involvement and soon people will feel confident to share memories aroused by the object they have chosen. Reminiscence quickly becomes an effective way of breaking down barriers because it is generally spontaneous, immediately infectious and enjoyable. The shared good fun and enthusiastic discussion encourage growth in confidence, which in turn raises participation levels.

Hearing problems

Hearing problems make participation in large groups extremely difficult. For this reason, groups should be kept small. Meeting places must be free of intrusive noise and, if possible, fitted with a loop system to assist people who wear hearing aids. If a person has a hearing aid that magnifies all noise, large noisy groups are intolerable. In a small group, however, with good lighting and appropriate seating to assist lip-reading and triggers that do not rely solely on sound, many deaf people will be able to enjoy a reminiscence group.

The visual stimulation provided by 35-mm slides or other projected images will have to be weighed against the disadvantage of reduced lighting that makes lip-reading impossible. Enlarged pictures and various other triggers that use sight, touch, taste and smell can, however, be very effective.

The level of frustration felt by people with acquired and progressive hearing loss is very varied. Some will enjoy being part of a small group, even if hearing is difficult. Others will be so frustrated over what they fear they are missing that their predicament is worsened. So select people very carefully and only after sensitive discussion with them about the likely obstacles and benefits.

Never shout when talking to a person with a hearing impairment. Clear, careful, well-modulated speech with rephrasing is more effective. When you shout, the increased volume means that the tone is usually raised. Because many older people lose their capacity to hear high tones and consonants, shouting does not help. Rather than repetition, rephrasing that uses different sound and lip patterns will increase the likelihood of being heard and hence understood.

Lip-reading classes for older people can make good use of reminiscence. Being interested in the subject matter, participants will listen more attentively and speak more freely. In this way, reminiscence assists learning, and lip-reading skills 'are caught, rather than taught'.

Provided that appropriate communication skills are used, people who were born deaf are as likely as anyone else to enjoy and profit from reminiscence. Ideally, trained interpreters who are also skilled reminiscence facilitators should be used, but this is not always possible. A compromise is for a reminiscence groupworker and an interpreter, sign language helper or lip-speaker, as appropriate, to work together as partners. Workers must get to know each other and to understand and respect each other's contribution. Different skills will be needed, as hearing-impaired people use many kinds of communication, including lip-reading, lip-speaking, finger-spelling, British Sign Language, Irish Sign Language, Sign Supported English, Paget Gorman, deafblind manual, block or total communication. People with speech and a learning disability generally use Makaton. Also remember that people from minority ethnic groups may not have mastered English or may in later life revert to their first language, and that impaired hearing will worsen any speech or language problems.

Amplification aids

Many different types of amplification aids are available. They include conventional and digital hearing aids, induction loops, battery-operated communicators and conversers, amplifiers and radio microphones. Seek advice and information from specialist workers such as speech and language therapists, hearing therapists, audiologists, special teachers, social workers for the deaf or medical specialists before buying any equipment.

Information and specialist services and assistance vary greatly in different geographic regions although legislation, the National Service Framework for Older People, Social Services guidelines for sensory impairment and the work of voluntary organisations are having an increasing impact. Advice and information are usually available from social services departments and specialist agencies such as the Royal National Institute for Deaf People (RNID), Sense, and the Disabled Living Foundation (see Appendix 2).

Visual problems

Reminiscence can be effective both with people who were born blind and with those who become visually impaired in later life. Very few people who lose their sight in late life are completely blind, even when registered as severely sight impaired/blind or as sight impaired/partially sighted. Most have some residual vision. Someone with glasses who can see only the top line of a sight chart or less at a distance of three metres could qualify for registration by an ophthalmologist as sight impaired/blind. If able to see the same line at 6 metres, they may be eligible for registration as sight impaired/partially blind. Various services and benefits are available to people so registered.

Free annual sight checks are available for anyone over 60, people over 40 with a family member with glaucoma and anyone with diabetes or who is registered blind or partially sighted. Understanding the different effects of various common visual problems will help the reminiscence worker to understand the specific problems of individuals, how they are affected and how to adapt reminiscence work to suit special needs and circumstances. It is important to offer early assistance, including the possibility of involving people in sociable reminiscence activities when they are first struggling to cope with visual loss and before depression may develop. Do not assume that you understand the particular problems people with impaired vision may be experiencing – ask them and then adjust how you seek to involve them in reminiscence in ways most likely to suit their special needs and circumstances.

Some common sight problems are described below.

Macular degeneration causes gradual loss of central vision, light sensitivity and, sometimes, visual hallucinations. Side (peripheral) vision remains normal, so it is possible to see things out of the corner of the eye but not straight in front. 'Dry' macular degeneration is untreatable although some sudden-onset 'wet' macular degeneration requires immediate specialist attention and may be treatable. Good lighting is essential; use contrasting colours, an adjustable lamp and magnifiers. Encourage looking out of the corner of the eye rather than directly ahead.

Cataract means the lens of the eye becomes clouded and vision becomes blurred, misty and dim. Seeing in bright light or changing light and in glare becomes increasingly difficult. Onset is gradual and treatment, usually by day surgery, has a high success rate. Avoidance of glare and use of sunglasses or hat and an adjustable lamp for close work may help.

Glaucoma results either in the extreme edges of the field of vision fading, so vision narrows, or in blank areas developing in the centre of the field of vision. Onset is gradual and reading may still be possible although the person may bump into things or seem clumsy. They will need strong but not glaring light and colour contrast. Magnifiers may help.

Diabetic retinopathy can result in patchy and blurred vision that may fluctuate from day to day or even hour to hour. It may produce variable floating spots or blurring. Laser treatment may be used and, sometimes, regular eye drops to heal and prevent further haemorrhages on the retina. Direct light shining straight into the eyes or light reflected from multiple sources or broken surfaces causes glare and should be avoided; hats, sunglasses and an adjustable lamp may assist.

Retinitis pigmentosa is an inherited, progressive, untreatable condition in which side or peripheral vision is lost, leaving only central vision or 'tunnel vision'. It causes night blindness and difficulty in seeing in dim or bright light and in adjusting to changes in light levels.

Afro-Caribbean and Asian people are more susceptible to diabetes and related visual conditions and glaucoma, and may develop these conditions at a younger age. Alertness to these possibilities and particular care and attention are necessary if you are hoping to undertake reminiscence work with members of these communities.

Using aids and adapting reminiscence

Many low-vision aids, ranging from simple magnifiers to very sophisticated technological aids, are available. As with hearing impairment, seek specialist advice. Information and assistance are available from opticians, doctors, specialist librarians, social services staff, rehabilitation officers, voluntary agencies such as the Royal National Institute of the Blind (RNIB) and other specialist agencies. (See Appendix 2 and Butler 2004 for more details.)

Visual images acquired during earlier life and laid down in memory can be used to evoke memories. The memories of people who have acquired blindness are often crystal clear, uncluttered by more recently acquired visual images. As a consequence, such people can be invaluable historical informants.

Butler (2004) recommends applying the three principles of brighter, bigger and bolder, which mean improve lighting, increase size and use contrasting colours. When presenting visual triggers, take account of how vision is affected by the various conditions described above and try to use people's peripheral and central vision appropriately. Objects that can be handled, tastes and smells, sounds – including reading aloud, listening to talking books and newspapers, music, audio tapes, CDs and DVDs – large-print books and enlarged visual triggers can all be used effectively. Non-verbal communication will be less successful than verbal communication. Computers with the capacity to change type fonts and select contrasting colours offer versatile opportunities for accessing relevant materials. Once again, specialist workers as either advisers or reminiscence partners can be invaluable.

Speech problems

Impaired speech greatly restricts opportunities for experiencing satisfying relationships and for participating in groups. Joy Harris (2005, page 121), a speech and language therapist, sums up the challenge:

'A speech and language disability is not one person's problem but a problem of anyone who comes into contact with that person.'

Reminiscence is a productive way of encouraging people who have impaired speech – regardless of what has caused the problem, be it a stroke, Parkinson's disease, dementia, learning disability or other condition – to talk. Talking about the past is especially useful with people who require speech practice following a stroke and whose family carers find that encouraging speech practice or even ordinary conversation is a dispiriting daily struggle. Although speech can be seriously affected by a stroke, memory may be little affected so it can be a useful tool that enables reminiscence to become an effective hook on which to hang attempts at conversation. As with lip-reading, if people are interested in what they are talking about, the amount of conversational effort they are prepared to exert can be significantly increased. When practice brings improvement, confidence increases.

Self-consciousness, low self-esteem and lack of confidence are often forgotten in the excitement of reminiscing. The person with the speech problem is able to share recall with others who in turn become less weary, frustrated or embarrassed by trying to persevere in conversation.

Try to obtain an assessment by a speech and language therapist through your local health centre or social services department so that you better understand the person's difficulties and how you may assist them. Problems with understanding (receptive) or with expressing (expressive) speech, or a mixture of both, will respond to different approaches. It is best to seek specialist advice. (Chapter 10 on dementia is also relevant.)

Work in pairs may be more appropriate than groupwork, but do not automatically rule out small group reminiscence. People should be given the chance to make their own choices, rather than have to endure decisions imposed by a professional who thinks they know best.

For example, a woman of 92 in a care home would often say: 'I don't speak so well since I had that stroke.' But as a member of a reminiscence group she spontaneously recited a long poem about the part of the country where she had farmed for many years. Other members were very moved and were quick to applaud: 'Marvellous. Marvellous. She has a good memory, anyhow.'

Some people, who cannot speak coherently, perhaps because of a stroke or dementia, may still be able to sing, probably because this area of their brain remains undamaged. It is well worth experimenting with singing in case it may be possible to encourage a singing response to 'conversational' singing that others initiate.

Conclusion

The greater the sensory and speech impairments and resulting communication problems, the greater the care you will need to take in selecting and assessing participants as well as locating and using suitable multi-sensory triggers and equipment. A detailed life history will help you to identify personal interests and relevant triggers, which must then be used in ways that will enable people to respond, despite their present disabilities. In our enthusiasm for knowing about a person's past, we must not neglect their needs in the immediate here and now, and much reminiscence-type conversation moves freely between the past and the present.

Printed and visual triggers, music, mime, gesture, demonstration, writing and drawing all have a part to play. Consult the person with the impairment and, after considering the best professional advice available, let your imagination run free. Follow your own intuition, good sense and sensitive inclinations in developing novel approaches to people who may otherwise remain extremely isolated and intensely frustrated.

KEY POINTS

■ Put the person before the impairment or disability. Listen carefully, observe closely and consult widely.

■ Try not to add to the disability by ignorance, insensitivity or ineptitude.

■ Do not make premature judgements that exclude people with sensory and speech impairments from opportunities to reminisce or to engage in related creative activities.

■ Obtain specialist advice, including information about methods of communication, technical equipment, aids and adaptations.

■ Seek out sensory, communication and rehabilitation specialists to work with you.

■ Develop non-verbal as well as verbal communication skills.

Application exercises

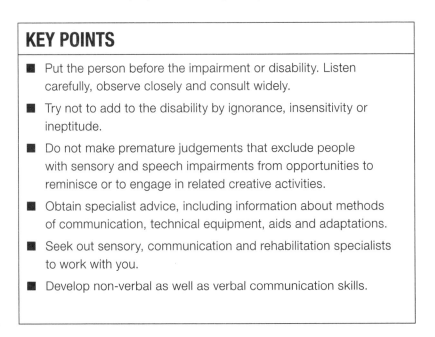

1 Identify a person with a hearing, visual or speech problem. Consider with them and other relevant people how best to involve them in reminiscence work. Implement your ideas and then discuss the outcomes with a colleague.

2 Read about hearing, visual and speech problems in later life. How can this new learning benefit the people with whom you work?

3 List ways in which you might adapt reminiscence activities to enable someone with multiple sensory disabilities to participate.

Further reading

Butler SJ. (2004) *Hearing and Sight Loss: A handbook for professional carers.* London: Age Concern Books

Mansfield J. (2005) *Effective Communication with People who have Hearing Difficulties.* Bicester: Speechmark

Parr S, Duchan J and Pound C. (2003) *Aphasia Inside Out: Reflections on communication disability.* Maidenhead: Open University

Taylor-Goh S (Ed). (2005) *Clinical Guidelines.* Bicester: Royal College of Speech and Language Therapists/Speechmark

13 Reminiscence with people with learning disabilities

Learning outcomes

After studying this chapter you should be able to:

* identify the benefits of reminiscence and life story work for people with learning disabilities
* locate, adapt, preserve and use relevant triggers
* assist in making tangible records of people's life stories
* become more alert to validating experiences of bereavement, loss and grief

The relevance of reminiscence

Reminiscence with people with learning disabilities fulfils many of the same general functions already described in Chapter 3. Each time planned reminiscence work with either individuals or groups is undertaken, the purpose and objectives need to be clear so that the worker(s) can explain clearly and concisely to the participants what is proposed. Published accounts of reminiscence work with people with moderate and severe learning disabilities demonstrate clearly that reminiscence work in small groups and life story work with individuals is greatly valued, indeed cherished, by many of those involved. Reminiscence enables people with learning disabilities, their families and carers to look back on their lives, recall past experience and reflect on what it means for themselves and for others.

Some modifications or adaptations are necessary, just as they have been necessary when working with other groups whose members have various disabilities. The guidance contained in earlier chapters on dementia, depression and sensory impairment is also relevant here. Professional staff members often report how surprised they are to find how well many people with a learning disability are able to participate in reminiscence. They stress how previously undemonstrated and unrecognised abilities emerge and personal confidence and self-esteem develop in reminiscence groups.

Michael Bender (1994), a psychologist, identified valuable outcomes for people with moderate and severe learning disabilities who participated in reminiscence groups – which he believes should meet for at least ten sessions. He noted:

- improvement in verbal ability;
- clear expression of strong emotions, particularly concerning experiences of loss;
- self-control and patience, contrary to usual behaviour;
- absence of socially unacceptable behaviour;
- abandonment, within the group, of usual roles and habitual ways of self-presentation;
- demonstration of a sense of agency, or control, over their own selves and circumstances.

The expression of loss and grief

When small reminiscence groups are held for adults with learning disabilities, many individual and collective recollections of painful memories, loss and grief are usually recounted. People with learning disabilities, especially as children and young people, even if living at home, are often protected from death in the family and not given opportunities by family and professional carers to mourn and to grieve openly when experiencing the death of a close relative. (See also Chapter 14.) Many also lack opportunities to talk frankly about their own experience of rejection and their awareness of being 'different' and how this has affected their lives.

In the past, many people with a learning disability who are now old were admitted to large institutions, often in infancy or childhood, thereby losing contact with their families, familiar people and the neighbourhoods where they once lived. Having spent most of their lives in long-stay hospitals, they were faced in mid-life or later with enormous changes as these hospitals closed. Many have been relocated in the community, in care homes, hostels, small group homes or independent flats. For most the changes in lifestyle have been dramatic.

Opportunities to mourn both the distant past and the more recent hospital past, no matter what it was like, are essential, and yet are often denied. The long-stay mental handicap hospitals in which people spent so much of their lives need to be actively acknowledged as a significant part of life experience and hence of memory. Except for the mental handicap hospital, many people with learning disabilities have no other sense of home or special place and its associated significant people (Atkinson, Jackson and Walmsley 1997).

Location, preservation and use of relevant triggers

The trigger materials used to encourage reminiscence should relate to the known past, wherever it has been lived. As hospitals contract, close or are demolished and residents are transferred or resettled, it is crucial that records and personal remembered accounts of this historical and personal heritage are preserved.

Collections of photographs portraying many aspects of hospital life usually exist somewhere, because these hospitals were themselves communities. It may be possible to locate photographs of holidays, sports days, trips, fêtes, farms, workshops, special occasions, staff and patients. Try to recover and preserve this heritage for the sake of the people whose lives are represented as well as reminders about the historical evolution of the National Health Service. For people who grew up in hospitals, staff and other patients were often a substitute family; for some, their only family. They will have many stories to tell, both good and bad, happy and sad, about nurses, patients, friends, ill-treatment, punishments, kindness, jobs, recreation, special events, and the whole complex life of the hospital as a living, if isolated, community.

Adapting reminiscence work

The same rules of good practice with individuals and groups apply to reminiscence work with people with learning disabilities and do not need to be repeated here. Groups will require co-workers, and individual life story work can often be improved and continuity assured if shared with more than one 'hearer'. When deciding on group membership, selection of people with a similar range of verbal abilities, including speed of speech, is recommended. It is not possible to be prescriptive about the number of sessions but at least ten and often many more are suggested. If it is planned to work on a group book or to help an individual person to make a record of their life story, several years may be necessary, as Dorothy Atkinson (1994), an oral historian and reminiscence facilitator, found.

Use carefully selected multi-sensory triggers. Tangible objects are usually very evocative. Do not overload people nor bombard them with questions. Adjust the pace of working and perhaps shorten the interval between sessions. Members' recollections will spark off other memories within the group so that at times a collective view, rather than a collection of individual memories, is achieved. Do not persist when attention span is limited. Be finely tuned to feelings. Help people express their pain, frustrations and joy in their own way, at their own pace.

If people with learning disabilities are taking part in a group with other members and leaders whose life experience has been very different, be alert to any lack of common interests or shared sympathies that may leave some people feeling inadequate or isolated. Alternatively, they may be surprised to discover that they too have a story to tell and others are interested in hearing it.

Reminiscence looks back, but effective work also concerns the present and invests in the future. As people accumulate new life experiences, make a record: be building for future memory work. Take photographs, collect memorabilia, help compile a diary and preserve the life history for future use. Make any records concrete, attractive, simple and direct.

Remember too that recreational group reminiscence activities may be fruitful. Trips, pilgrimages, dances, organised games and outings may all be used to reinforce a sense of personal identity, to give pleasure, to increase sociability, to assist communication and to lay down or encode pleasurable memories.

The importance of making a tangible record

Life story work is particularly relevant because of its emphasis on making tangible, practical, written, audio or pictorial records of a personal history.

Never take for granted, or fail to appreciate, the fact that you can write your own story. If you choose to, you are capable of giving your own account and making your own record. People with learning disabilities may be able to tell you about themselves but may be unable to either write or read their stories. Do not assume this means that the tangible, durable record is not valued. Its importance must never be underestimated.

The process of recall is important but so too is the sense of permanence and significance that the product or record conveys. It is immensely prized, as Doreen Cocklin testified when her revealing spoken-but-written observations were published in an anthology of prose, poetry and art by people with learning disabilities: 'This is the first time anything I have said has been written down' (Atkinson and Williams 1990, page 9). In commenting on the project in which Doreen Cocklin participated, these authors (page 8) commented:

> *'The use of reminiscence enables people to emerge not as victims but as survivors; not as people deficient in skills or requisite social behaviour but as individuals with a personal history, a culture, a class, a gender, as well as an impairment.'*

There will be a heavy reliance on the spoken, rather than the written, word. Some people may be able to write but many will need a scribe or supporter if they are to present their work in a way that makes it possible for others to appreciate it.

To assist the writing, reminiscence and life history workers frequently use a tape recorder and then a 'scribe' becomes responsible for producing the record. These transcriptions need to be read back, meticulously corrected or changed to make sure the story is being told as its owner intended. A copy of the tape and the transcript should always be given to the person to keep but can then be used effectively as a prompt for further reminiscence and recall.

Community publishing and desktop publishing have meant that increasing numbers of 'silent' or 'invisible' people, not only those with learning disabilities, can now have their stories published, read and more widely appreciated. These accounts are significant contributions to developing understanding of others' experience, and the ways in which marginalised and excluded people have been denied past opportunities, so easily taken for granted by most of us.

The life story is important for the teller but it is also important for the hearer – herein lies the mutual gain for all involved, as Mabel Cooper (2005, page 36) demonstrates. She was born in 1944, admitted to a children's home as a baby, transferred, aged 12, to St Lawrence's Mental Handicap Hospital and then, after some 20 years, relocated in the community via time spent in a half-way hostel. She now lives with a family, chairs the London Consultative Group (a self-advocacy group), visits schools to talk about her life, travels internationally and undertakes consultancy and staff training.

> ***Mabel Cooper*** *'When I started to do my life story, very few people like me had been able to tell their stories. I know only of one other man from the hospital who wrote about his life. I think it is important that people who lived in the institutions tell their stories because then you get to know what life was like for people like me in them days. I looked at my files at the hospital. I've got them now. Some of it is terrible – like the names what they called us in them days. But the records don't tell you what life was like on the wards. And museums don't have that information either; so if we don't tell people through our books, people won't ever know.'*

Atkinson (1998, page 73) helped Mabel Cooper and other women with learning disabilities to write their stories, and she describes the complexity of the process for both teller and hearer.

> ***Mabel Cooper, the teller*** *'It was very important to me to tell them about St Lawrence's and the way it was when I was there.'*

> ***Dorothy Atkinson*** *'(We) have been touched, moved and angered by their revelations. These stories have helped open our eyes to what life has been like for those people who, in the earlier years of the [20th] century, had the misfortune to enter the separate and closed world of the long-stay institutions.*

'For as we get to know those who share their reminiscences and their life stories with us, we too gain, not just knowledge or vicarious experience but an enlargement of our capacity to feel with others whose lives have been, and may still be, very different from our own.'

This work is complex and demanding. It is important to consider very carefully what people who are reminiscing actually say while they are reminiscing. You have to ask yourself what meaning the story has for the teller in the here and now. It will be a story about the past but it will be told in a particular way in the present. This applies to all reminiscence but is particularly relevant to reminiscence with people with learning disabilities and people with dementia who are likely to have difficulty in explaining the meanings themselves or perhaps clearly distinguishing the past and the present.

The listener always influences the story that people tell. The teller and the hearer are both creators of the story and no talk is meaningless. People with learning disabilities also have a story to tell. They, as much as anyone else, need someone to ask and someone to listen.

Life story books

Creating a life story book is not a routine mechanical technique but rather a carefully focused individual intervention whose purpose is to capture the 'real' person – not to write a clinical report. Such books are relevant regardless of the level of intellectual disability of the person concerned. Helen Hewitt (2003, page 19), a nurse educator, stresses that 'Each person's life story book should be approached with a fresh view to emphasise the uniqueness of that person.'

The story of a person's past life and relationships has helped to shape their present needs, desires and aspirations. If information is carefully documented in a life book, it can be a valuable working tool as well as a historical record. It can:

- contribute to person-centred care planning;
- help to define the person as a person rather than as a service user, patient or resident;

- identify what is important to the person in the present;
- serve as a communication tool for people who may find it difficult to express themselves;
- help the person clarify issues concerning their past and present identity that label the person as disabled;
- help acknowledge past complex issues or abusive relationships;
- decrease barriers and increase mutual understanding between service users and providers;
- assist people to make sense of the past so as to function in the present and face the future;
- identify the person's need for help in dealing with whatever issues emerge;
- assist new carers to understand and to know the person as a unique individual.

There is no one preferred format for such a book although a scrapbook approach is fairly common. (See also Chapter 6.) There are three stages in the process:

1 information gathering
2 interpreting the information
3 presenting the information

Hewitt (2000) suggests that all information-gathering interviews should be recorded and that they should be undertaken with any available people who had known the person at any stage – family members, neighbours and staff members. The informants should be encouraged to bring any relevant photographs and artefacts to the interview. Hewitt cautions against altering the stories in any way or being concerned about establishing accuracy. She suggests that the following themes can be covered in one or two interviews with an informant whereas Atkinson stresses working directly with the subject person (and other informants) over a more extended period of time:

- birth story;
- life as a baby and young child;
- early memories and experiences;

- favourite things;
- relationships with families and friends;
- places lived;
- happy memories;
- significant life events and other family members.

A hand-written book, Hewitt suggests, may be more likely to be added to in the future than either a typed or word-processed book which tends to create the impression of being finished or complete.

It is vital that the supporter, scribe or assistant (and each word describes a different facet of the essential relationship) must create trust and respect and be clear about the task. The person being assisted must remain in control, feeling secure in the process and free to withdraw at any time. The content should always be read back and adjusted according to the person's wishes or instructions.

Ageing parents of people with all kinds of learning disability worry greatly about the future care of their children. They too can be encouraged and assisted to prepare a record of their own lives as a means of resolving their own issues and informing future carers and as a legacy for their adult child. A starting point for such sensitive exploration could be for the parent to be invited to consider 'what would I like other people to know about – throughout his or her life and what would I like – to remember or to be reminded about me and our family?'

Down's syndrome and dementia

Advances in medical and social care have resulted in increased life expectancy for people with learning difficulties. People with Down's syndrome are now living longer and consequently they risk developing age-related conditions, especially dementia, at an earlier age than either people with other learning disabilities or the general population (Janicki and Dalton 1999). Indications of dementia include the loss of various skills and alterations in mood, short-term memory and sleep patterns. People affected have many different and changing needs. Early detection and appropriate assessment are essential so that other conditions such as depression or thyroid malfunction can be treated or eliminated.

Individual life story work and group reminiscence have important contributions to make to continuing care. Ideally it is desirable for people affected by dementia to receive additional support that will enable them to continue to live in their family home or group home (Kerr 1997). If this is not possible, a life story book becomes an invaluable introduction to new carers.

Helping other residents of a group home to understand about dementia, and to remember the life and times shared with the resident who develops it, may help achieve 'ageing in place' – continuing to live in the same place. Because inappropriate, unfamiliar or unsympathetic environments can hasten deterioration and loss of confidence, remaining in familiar surroundings with well-known companions and committed familiar staff is much preferred. This is usually considered to be better than transfer to a care home that will accommodate substantially older people and where the special needs of a younger person with Down's syndrome or other learning disability are not always understood. Listening to and knowing each person's story helps staff carers to focus on the person rather than their disabilities.

Because people with Down's suffer premature ageing and as approximately one-third of them are likely to develop dementia, they, their families and professional carers should be encouraged to start a life story book as soon as possible, even in late childhood, adolescence or young adulthood. It can then be added to throughout the person's lifetime as well as being used as a record, a memory jogger, a communication tool and a passport for introducing the person to hospital or care home staff should a move become necessary at any time (Hopkins 2002).

Security and continuity, based on long-established familiarity, are cornerstones of good care. If these are not possible, it is crucial that the person and their new carers have a readily available tool such as a life story book from which to glean the fine-grained personal detail of the person's life – rarely found or easily located in a case record or medical notes.

Conclusion

Reminiscence and life story work, suitably modified and using various approaches and formats, are very important for people with learning disabilities of all kinds. Assisting people who have life-long intellectual disabilities to value themselves by recovering, recording and valuing their memories of past experiences is emotionally demanding work. Facilitators must respect the views and wishes of the people concerned and exercise considerable empathy and personal discipline in working as supporters in the process of reminiscing and creating records. It is important to begin this work as early as possible in each person's lifetime and regardless of the severity of the disability. People with Down's syndrome have an increased risk of developing dementia, and life story books can be especially useful for preserving their stories and reminding them of significant places, people, possessions and events in their lives. Family carers also may find that working on their own life stories in addition to contributing to their child's story can be very helpful.

KEY POINTS

- The past is important for people with learning disabilities.
- They should have their experience of grief and loss acknowledged, not denied.
- Work in imaginative ways to help people to achieve a tangible record.
- This record, in turn, becomes a tool for continuing communication.
- A life story book is crucial for people with Down's syndrome, who have an increased risk of developing dementia at a much earlier age than the general population or people with other types of learning disability.

Application exercises

1   Identify a person with a learning disability with whom you could work to compile a record of his or her life story. Collect stories, photographs and memorabilia as well as actively preserving information now that will become part of the 'record' for the future.

2   Identify the ways you may need to adapt general and specific reminiscence work for individuals and small groups of people who have learning disabilities.

3   Reflect on the impact that the life story of a person with a learning disability has made on you.

Further reading

Atkinson D (Ed). (2000) *Good Times, Bad Times: Women with learning difficulties telling their stories.* Kidderminister: Bild Publications

Black Friendly Group. (2004) *Telling it Ourselves: An oral history.* London: Joseph Rowntree Foundation [video and booklet]

Down's Syndrome Association. (2004) *Ageing and its Consequences for People with Down's Syndrome: A guide for parents and carers.* London: Down's Syndrome Association

Hewitt H. (2000) 'A life story approach for people with profound learning disabilities', *British Journal of Nursing* **9** (2): 90–95

Stuart M. (1997) *Looking Back, Looking Forward: Reminiscence with people with learning disability.* Brighton: Pavilion Publishing

Wilkinson H, Kerr D, Cunningham C and Rae C. (2004) *Home for Good?* Brighton: Pavilion/Joseph Rowntree

14 Reminiscence with terminally ill and bereaved people

Learning outcomes

After studying this chapter you should be able to:

- understand the relevance of reminiscence and life review for people facing terminal illness or bereavement
- appreciate the complexities of grief for bereaved people who have dementia or a learning disability
- realise that, although loss is an ever-present part of being human and death is one of the few certainties in life, coping with both makes heavy demands on carers and reminiscence workers

Loss and grief

Loss means to be separated from, to be unable to locate or to have something taken away. Some losses are validated by society and some are not. Overcoming loss and grief is very much more complicated if the loss is denied or unrecognised by others.

There are many different kinds of loss. These include loss of significant others, body image (how we see ourselves), relationships, money, pets, possessions, places, and unfulfilled ambitions and opportunities. The actual loss itself has to be endured as well as the subsequent physical, social and psychological upsets that accompany it. Whilst death is an event, bereavement is the process of experiencing the associated loss. Grief is the accompanying emotion that comes with loss, change and readjustment, and it affects people in physical, emotional and behavioural ways. People experience bereavement and grief in many different ways and at varying speeds. Although some pattern may be recognisable (Parkes 1986), there is no such thing as a standard journey through bereavement or a rigid 'grieve by' date.

Lorna Baker (2004, page 82), who records individual's life stories for families, writes:

> 'Several times an elderly person has grieved afresh at remembering the loss of a loved one very many years earlier. It had been a wound carried all that time. I remember 89-year-old Ivy welled up when speaking about her father, who died when she was only four years old.'

Sharing memories assists people to share emotions. A life review helps to bring a life to a close because in the process the person comes to understand what their life has meant, or, put another way, they come to find meaning in life and meaning in their own life. Being listened to and being able to recount aspects of the past, many people suggest, helps to lessen present pain and reduce current anxiety, at least to some extent.

Some people with a terminal diagnosis are able to live for the day and make the most of the time that is left, without experiencing overwhelming anxiety about the future. They will reach this place of acceptance – or 'integrity' to use Erikson's term – by many different routes and by using diverse means. These can include talking with trusted people, recording a life story, life review, writing, doing a guided autobiography or a spiritual autobiography, painting or music depending upon their personal values, relationships, spirituality, opportunities and resources. Acceptance of the past and understanding its impact on the present seem to be a crucial part of such acceptance.

The Mothers' Living Stories Project

This Project aims to help mothers living with cancer or some other life-threatening or chronic illness to review their lives, usually over six weekly sessions in which they are assisted by trained volunteer listeners. They are helped to audio record their living stories as legacies for their children. The process offers healing for the mother, a means of opening communication with the family and a cherished gift for children and loved ones (Blachman 2003). More information can be found on: www.motherslivingstories.org

When a couple is facing the terminal illness of one partner, joint life review work seems to be an obvious choice. This, however, may not always be the best choice. Parallel life reviews may more adequately meet the separate needs of each partner. Issues of choice, autonomy and control require careful consideration. Partners may be at different stages of their shared and separate journeys into grief and may need different and separate opportunities to face what each is going through.

Parents of dying children, it has been suggested, can be helped ahead of the child's eventual terminal stage to endure their own grief in anticipation. As the needs of the dying child become more urgent, the parent is freer and more available to the child because at least some of their grieving has now been done. Such thinking may also apply sometimes to adult partnerships, especially where the illness is lengthy, hope of recovery long abandoned and some emotional restoration has replaced earlier grief.

Unacknowledged or disenfranchised grief

Just like others, people with a learning disability or dementia also experience loss, bereavement and grief but they are often denied the opportunity to understand what has happened, to express their emotions and to mourn openly. 'Disenfranchised grief' refers to grief that is not openly acknowledged, is not socially validated or publicly mourned. Too often the grief of people with a learning disability or dementia is denied because, being overprotected by well-meaning if mistaken others, they are prevented from participating in mourning rituals such as sending flowers, writing letters of condolence, sending mass cards or attending funerals.

The death of a main carer can have devastating effects for people with a learning disability or dementia because, in addition, it may entail the loss of home, independence, familiar people, places and possessions. Frequently it will entail relocation with all the attendant strangeness, upset, disruption of familiar routines and new surroundings.

If a main carer or close friend has a terminal illness, the person with a learning disability or dementia may also be debarred from saying goodbye or preparing themselves for what is to come. Their cognitive difficulties may also limit their comprehension but it is wrong to assume they do not understand at some level or will soon forget the loved person. Doka (2002) suggests that people with a learning disability are disenfranchised in grief. So too are many children and many people with dementia. Such people need special help to acknowledge and to cope openly with their grief. Working through a life story book, memory book or photographic collection in which the deceased person features, drawing, and sharing poetry, music, stories and reminiscence can all assist people to acknowledge and express their thoughts and feelings.

Listening to music with terminally ill people

Playing music of personal relevance can open up conversation between people who may otherwise find it difficult to speak of matters of great personal importance when facing terminal illness. Music can provide a link between people and help them access memories and related emotions. It encourages conversation or provides a comforting background when words are unnecessary or impossible. It also stimulates lethargic people, stuck in the inertia of illness and grief – provided that the music is culturally acceptable and reflects the personal faith and immediate needs of the dying person and the family. Encouraging a family to compile a tape or CD of a person's preferred music that reflects lifetime preferences at different ages and stages can be a useful tool at the end of life for bringing comfort and easing grief.

Pickles (2005) suggests that we all have several 'selves' rather than just one self and that our 'musical self' remains resilient as disease, including dementia, progresses. Just as personhood depends on relationships with others who must affirm and interact, so too does the 'musical self'. To listen, sing or play alone may be helpful but done in the company of an understanding friend or 'musical companion' it will be much more effective and personally affirming and comforting.

Guidelines for addressing grief

- respect the bereaved person, regardless of disability and age;
- openly recognise and acknowledge grief;

- provide accurate and truthful information and repeat as and when necessary;
- adjust communication to the person's age, abilities, understanding and culture;
- encourage participation in mourning rituals;
- use tangible and verbal reminders of recalled memories;
- provide continuing, respectful and appreciative support.

Reasons for reminiscing at times of terminal illness and bereavement

In these circumstances, many people seek to find meaning in life and in their own life. They want to express their deepest feelings but may find this difficult to do. Reminiscence will help a person to identify and celebrate achievements, to say goodbye, express regrets and make amends (Jones, Lyons and Cunningham 2003).

Reminiscence helps people to recognise the values by which they have lived and the messages they wish to bequeath to others. At this time family members and close friends who encourage and share in reminiscing can show that they value the dying person and the journey taken through life. The benefit of doing this extends way beyond the person's death and has implications for those who survive, and possibly for descendants not yet born.

> *'Survivors can share the deceased elder's legacy in a spiritual reflection that occurs as part of a celebration of their life and death. It is only as people who have cared for us reach the end of life that we see the full gift that we have received from them. By leaving us their reminiscences, their spirits can continue in our lives as a living memorial.'* (Grudzen and Soltys 2000, page 8)

Reminiscing during bereavement and in the years ahead is a way of maintaining continuing bonds with the dead person or, in Webster's phrase, for 'intimacy maintenance'.

People with dementia and terminal illness

When a person has both dementia and cancer or other life-threatening condition, their family and professional carers face many complex demands. To provide adequate physical care, including pain relief, when communication is impaired is demanding enough but meeting the emotional needs of the person and their family members is exceedingly onerous. Being unable to verbalise their fears, hopes and experience of pain, anxiety, depression, frustration and aggression may develop or worsen.

Can reminiscence and life review contribute anything at this time? Many people have written about the loneliness of dying and the tendency for family members to withdraw or to distance themselves as the end approaches – as John Causley, the poet, said of his father's death: 'A lonely man goes out alone'. Too often, making meaning of the sum of our days is a solitary occupation when instead 'as death nears, one needs to interact to mirror back the meaning of life' (Barrett and Soltys 2002, page 63).

Isolation and loneliness are likely to be even greater for a person affected by dementia and their carer. Frequently people with dementia are considered to be socially dead, emotionally disconnected, long before physical death overtakes them. As long as some verbal capacity remains, talking about the past may make talking in the present more possible and so help postpone the eventual parting of the ways – the end of a shared journey. A family carer's own anxiety, depression and extreme fatigue are likely to be considerable at this time and will limit the effort they are able to make. Research suggests that pre-existing depression of a carer foreshadows a poor outcome from the eventual bereavement, so attention to the carer's needs in their own right is very important.

Engagement in reminiscence by a spouse or partner with their adult children (or grandchildren) is one way of maintaining relationships and lessening isolation. It can also assist the grieving spouse, partner and others to come to terms with both the past and the present. They can be encouraged to recall the positives and put the negatives to rest, and remember and remind themselves of past times spent with the dying or deceased person. Engagement in a structured life review may help the bereaved or grieving person to value himself or herself at a time when self-esteem, competence and confidence are being threatened. (See Chapter 6.)

Spouses or partners of people who develop dementia commonly experience anticipatory grief. Long before the person dies, the carer has faced the inevitable decline when confronted daily with evidence of increasing cognitive and physical frailty. A structured life review with the carer will assist them to identify past strengths and past coping, and possibly achieve resolution, and sometimes reconciliation, in the present. Undertaking a structured life review at this stage is an investment by the spouse or partner in his or her own mental health if only they can find sufficient energy to set aside time for this task. Although attention to family needs is now common in hospice care of cancer patients, where openness, sharing, death preparation and acknowledgement of the influence of the past on the present are encouraged in family members, similar opportunities are still extremely rare in dementia care services.

In the terminal stage of dementia, the person will have little residual speech so two-way conversation is bound to be limited, although not always impossible. Carers have reported astonishing moments of psychological clarity in end-stage dementia. Usually family carers will need someone else other than the dying person with whom to share their story at this time. This could be a professional carer, sometimes a family member, the relatives of other patients or a highly skilled volunteer.

Professionals need to recognise that the family carer of a terminally ill person who is dying from end-stage dementia or, more likely, from some other condition such as pneumonia or cancer, also has complex and multiple needs. The listener must be able to encourage the family carer to talk and be open to hear the story. As well as having someone to listen, at this time the family carer also needs to help the dying person, and be assured they are comfortable and pain free. The family carer should be kept informed of deterioration and impending death; they need to be able to air their emotions and to find comfort, support and acceptance for themselves, what they are experiencing and what they have to face.

Conclusion

Disenfranchised grief imposed on children, people with learning disabilities and people who have dementia does them a grave disservice. Grief denied is unlikely to be experienced constructively. Increasingly it is recognised that opportunities for engaging in conversation, mourning rituals and open grieving better promote the long-term mental health of bereaved people. The needs of terminally ill people for reviewing their lives and preparing for death are complex and demanding. So too are the needs of family members who also may be helped by means of reminiscence, life review and related creative activities. The terminal care of people who have both dementia and other life-threatening conditions is not well understood, and the needs of their family carers frequently remain inadequately addressed.

KEY POINTS

■ It is important to create opportunities for people to tell their life stories before it is too late.

■ Do not attempt to prevent children or people with learning disabilities or dementia from openly participating in the funeral arrangements of a loved person.

■ Disenfranchised grief can create long-enduring problems.

■ Use reminiscence, life review and related creative activities to assist terminally ill people and their family carers, either separately or jointly, to value their shared lives. Wherever possible, encourage the production of some form of tangible record.

Application exercises

1 Discuss this chapter with a trusted friend or colleague. What do you think of the suggestions it contains about doing reminiscence and life review work with people with a terminal illness and their family carers?

2 Identify a person who you think may be enduring disenfranchised grief. How might you seek to encourage them to share their memories of a deceased person?

3 Encourage an isolated chronically or terminally ill person to share their life story with you, and if possible assist them to make a record.

Further reading

Blackman N (Ed). (1999) *Living with Loss: Helping people with learning disabilities cope with loss and bereavement.* Brighton: Pavilion Publishing

Bright R. (1996) *Grief and Powerlessness: Helping people regain control of their lives.* London: Jessica Kingsley

Doka KJ. (2002) *Disenfranchised Grief: New directions, challenges and strategies for practice.* Champaign, IL: Research Press

Jenkins C and Merry J. (2005) *Relative Grief.* London: Jessica Kingsley

15 **Staff development, training, quality and evaluation issues**

Learning outcomes

After studying this chapter you should be able to:

- develop an action plan for doing reminiscence work
- appreciate the importance of reminiscence training, support and supervision
- undertake networking and develop partnerships for sharing ideas, resources and skills
- complete a simple evaluation of a reminiscence group/project

Developing a reminiscence action plan

It is almost impossible to develop good practice as a reminiscence facilitator if you are working in isolation. Gather colleagues and friends around you who will support, encourage and sustain each other's work.

Develop your own local resource materials. Start where you are with the people with whom you want to reminisce. Collect triggers that will mean something to them. Use commercially marketed triggers only if you are unable to obtain your own or if you want to extend your own collection without too much trouble. Commercial packages will get you started and give you ideas but they are usually expensive. The same amount of money spent on acquiring local resources may give better returns.

Local schools and further education colleges, community arts organisations, libraries and museums may have digital cameras, recording equipment, photographic dark rooms, colour photocopiers, computers with scanners, laser printers and other useful equipment. They will also have expertise and may be very pleased to cooperate as partners in a reminiscence project. In return you may be able to help extend their oral archives by identifying older people willing to become historical informants and informal teachers, mentors and volunteers. You may also be able to create opportunities for younger students to undertake community service. Various aspects of the curriculum, not just history or community studies, can be enriched through the involvement of older people. (See Chapters 7, 8 and 9.)

Partnerships between different agencies that bring together the statutory and independent service sectors can release creative energy to help develop and sustain reminiscence work. Staff members from local libraries and museums can be invaluable allies. There are a lot of resources available to help you develop good reminiscence practice but there are no short cuts. Appendix 2 gives contact details of some relevant organisations.

Sharing resources

Do not hog your triggers or monopolise resources. Try to form a local group or network that meets from time to time to share ideas, constructively criticise work in progress and pool assets. You will all be the richer for sharing and, as a consequence, the quality and nature of the reminiscence work you do will benefit.

This handbook has stressed cooperation. It emphasises the importance of both informal collaboration and formal supervision, which itself may take different forms such as tandem or paired, team and group supervision. Find people whom you can trust to be honest with you, not tell you what you want to hear. Only by looking critically at your practice will you become more skilled. Initial training before you begin is important but further training needs to be linked to practice so that critical reflection becomes an integral part of your on-going development.

The importance of reminiscence

As well as continuing to develop reminiscence work in hospitals, care homes and day centres, it is increasingly important to help families, friends, volunteer visitors and domiciliary care workers to understand how significant the past is and how they can encourage people to talk about it. As the practice of care in the community expands, older frailer people are being helped to remain in their own homes. As a consequence, we can expect an increasing amount of reminiscence work to be undertaken with individuals living in the community.

Care management arrangements, strict financial controls, the narrow definition of functional tasks and associated rationing of time spent by health and social care staff bring increasing pressures. These can too often work against the development of good reminiscence practice. The tendency to regard care as a commodity and its recipients as consumers has many associated life-limiting implications. This book does not apologise for arguing that older people's minds and souls (or spirits) need nourishment as much as their bodies do. Relationships nurtured by care, concern and effective communication are essential. Reminiscence and other creative activities are not expendable luxuries; they are life-sustaining essentials.

Evaluation and research

Both qualitative and quantitative methodologies are needed in researching reminiscence undertaken in different cultures and contexts of practice, and with different types of reminiscers. Likewise, the preparation and training of reminiscence workers also requires to be researched so that our knowledge, understanding and skill continue to develop. So far, most research has concentrated on outcomes with older people. The functions served by reminiscence for men and women at earlier stages of the life cycle who face various problematic circumstances and health conditions also need to be researched. Different ways of supporting reminiscence workers and the effect of doing reminiscence on staff, on family carers and on volunteers still awaits systematic enquiry.

Reminiscence and life review with children, adolescents and young adults also requires exploration. Reminiscence practice with prisoners, refugees, asylum seekers, people who have endured extreme trauma, have AIDS-related dementia, or dementia linked to learning disability and trauma-induced brain damage may also be fruitful fields of enquiry. The processes of reminiscence as much as its outcomes require careful scrutiny. We need to learn more about the complex interdependence of the cognitive and creative aspects of reminiscence and recall, and how to harness this energy to improve communication, nurture relationships and enhance well-being. The who, what, when, where, how and why of reminiscence and life review all require further systematic investigation by practitioner researchers and research groups that include practitioners and reminiscence participants working alongside skilled researchers.

The evaluation process

If reminiscence knowledge and skills are to develop, reminiscence practitioners need to be open to having their work scrutinised by others and to be willing and able to engage in its systematic evaluation. Workers' self-evaluation is important and should involve critical examination of all the stages involved in reminiscence work. Northen and Kurland (2001, page 448) identify the ingredients of successful groupwork: 'Competence evolves out of commitment, curiosity and the thirst for knowledge.'

The following questions may help guide your evaluation of a reminiscence group/project; the same questions could be adapted for evaluating work with an individual or couple. Forms 2, 3, 4 and 5 in Appendix 1 can be used to record and evaluate the responses of participants week by week, as scored by the leaders or facilitators.

1 Planning

- What needs did the participants have that led to the decision to involve them in reminiscence work?
- What did you (the worker) want them to achieve?
- Were the identified objectives achieved?
- How well did the chosen structure match the needs and aspirations of the participants?

2 Beginning phase

- How well did you manage to set up an effective context in which to work?
- How well did the members understand the agreed purposes and programme?
- What ground rules were established and in what ways did they contribute to the group?

3   Middle phase

- How well did you understand each member's needs, strengths and problems?
- What was the quality of your relationship with each member?
- How well did you display genuineness, empathy, acceptance and respect?
- To what extent did the group achieve its intended tangible and intangible outcomes?
- To what extent did members discover common ground and respect differences?
- To what extent did you exercise reminiscence skills?

4   Ending phase

- To what extent did you adequately prepare each member and yourself for the group's ending?
- To what extent and in what ways did the group evaluate its own process and outcomes?
- What would you plan to do differently or to change in your approach and leadership style next time you undertake reminiscence work?

Reminiscence training, support and supervision

The training, recognition and continued development of reminiscence and related work remains largely unorganised, diffuse and educationally incoherent. As far as is known, there is no distinct reminiscence qualification registered by the Qualification and Curriculum Authority in the UK.

Ad hoc short courses

A large number of short training events, conferences and courses, many of which award attendance certificates, are offered by various statutory and voluntary organisations, educational establishments, and private sector and self-employed trainers and consultants. These training events vary greatly in level, duration, content and objectives. If short courses are to secure financial support from employers and attract staff, they must demonstrate relevance to national occupational standards.

Reminiscence training is often arranged in response to local requests and takes place in many different venues, including health and social care agencies, community groups, libraries, museums and colleges. It may involve only staff of a specific agency, or recruitment may be on a multi-agency and multi-professional basis. Various organisations offering local or regional training courses are listed in Appendix 2, which does not claim to be comprehensive. Local and regional training creates opportunities to establish links with other interested people who can offer mutual support and encouragement. Such networking is invaluable in developing personal confidence and competence as practitioners and for promoting the wider development of reminiscence work. (See also Chapter 7.)

Age Exchange

Age Exchange offers a long-established training programme in many aspects of reminiscence practice, and trainers will work with staff members in their places of work to help them to establish reminiscence projects (see Appendix 2).

European Reminiscence Network

The European Reminiscence Network maintains a database of workers and provides opportunities through workshops, cross-national projects, publications, training programmes, theatre tours and international conferences for people to share experience and develop creative, innovative practice.

Open College

The Open College accredits a small number of assessed reminiscence courses linked to related practice experience (see National Open College Network in Appendix 2 for contact details).

NVQ and SVQ training for the health and social care workforce

Reminiscence practice and preparation for undertaking it with individuals, families, groups and communities can form part of various core and optional units within the NVQ and SVQ frameworks. NVQs and SVQs form a part of training provision designed to reflect the job functions of the social care workforce. Different NVQ levels have been matched to various occupational roles and to the skills required to fulfil these roles. The Social Care Councils for Scotland, Wales and Northern Ireland, but not the General Social Care Council for England, link with the Sector Skills Council for the care sector, which is responsible for ensuring skill development. In England, the Children's Workforce Development Council and Skills for Care, which represents the adult social care work force, are the link bodies. See the Resources section for information about other responsibilities fulfilled by the four Social Care Councils, which operate under their respective Departments of Health.

The past impacts in innumerable ways on people's present lives, needs and circumstances. This means that knowledge of the past, gained by means of participation in life review and reminiscence work, can be central to understanding present functioning and meeting various aspects of present need. Reminiscence competencies are therefore relevant elements in meeting the requirements of many NVQ and SVQ units in Health and Social Care (Adults) at Levels 2, 3 and 4. Underpinning knowledge acquired through reminiscence training, which is evidenced by practice and critical reflection, can contribute towards many different units.

The relevant units apply to working with people of various ages and circumstances, including those who are older, physically or cognitively disabled, or mentally ill, or have sensory, speech or learning impairments. Other units concerned with supporting family carers and volunteers may also be relevant. Level 4 units that require candidates to carry responsibility for implementation of work are equally, if not more, relevant for experienced reminiscence workers. Life story work with children and young people also meets some of the requirements of Level 3 Children's Units. There are too many appropriate units to list, so consult line managers or workplace assessors if you wish to include reminiscence work as part of NVQ assessments.

University courses

Open University The OU's Level 1 certificate course, Understanding Health and Social Care, carries 60 Cats points and relates to NVQ and SVQ Levels 3 and 4 in health and social care. It is designed to provide the knowledge, skills and understanding required in caring work of all kinds. The study block 'Working with Life Experience' is of special relevance to reminiscence work. (For further information, see contact details in Appendix 2.)

University of Sussex As a leading international centre for the study of life history, oral history and life story work, the University of Sussex offers various taught courses at taster, certificate, degree and postgraduate levels on a part-time and a full-time basis. Research degrees of MPhil and DPhil are also offered. (For further information, see contact details in Appendix 2.)

Post-registration of the social care workforce

Reminiscence courses that offer teaching and opportunity for the compilation of evidence of critical reflection on related practice may be suitable for inclusion in Post-registration and Learning Records of Evidence and Achievement. The four National Social Care Councils require these records as a condition of continued registration. Registrants are now required by law to complete 15 days or 90 hours of study, training or other activities shown to contribute to professional development and life-long learning when renewing their registration every three years. Registrants must maintain a record of their training and learning achievements throughout their career, and they may be asked to provide evidence of such training at the time of re-registration.

This new requirement provides opportunities for informal, ad hoc reminiscence training events, as well as longer, more formal, post-registration courses and training opportunities to be credited. Registered workers are required to keep documented evidence to demonstrate how such training/developmental opportunities relate to and contribute to an explicit training and learning plan. Such plans are usually agreed with employers, who are now obliged to provide opportunities for the continuing professional development for their social care staff.

Conclusion

Do continue to read about reminiscence work. Follow up the references and the suggestions in the 'Further reading' lists at the end of each chapter. As you read, try to distinguish between reports of actual reminiscence work, empirical research studies, particular methods or approaches and theory-building articles. You will be able to learn from research articles and analyses of good practice but when you go to apply the ideas you will need to copy, as best you can, the same conditions described in the article in order to try out the same approach. Reading about reminiscence work will give you new ideas about fresh directions as well as increasing your confidence in what you are doing.

Remember that one meaning of 'professional' is trying to do better tomorrow what you have done today. No matter how well your work has gone so far, you will still be able, next time, to become a more attentive and empathic listener, a more sensitive, skilled worker. Consolidate your development by undertaking further reminiscence work and training. In this way you will build on what you have already learned rather than letting it become submerged or forgotten by other pressing demands on your time and attention.

To help you look to your future reminiscence work, with all its rich possibilities for benefiting both yourself and other people, you may like to complete one last exercise.

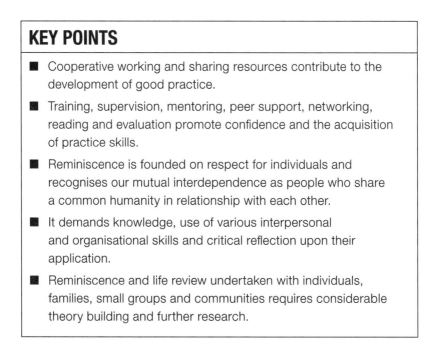

KEY POINTS

- Cooperative working and sharing resources contribute to the development of good practice.

- Training, supervision, mentoring, peer support, networking, reading and evaluation promote confidence and the acquisition of practice skills.

- Reminiscence is founded on respect for individuals and recognises our mutual interdependence as people who share a common humanity in relationship with each other.

- It demands knowledge, use of various interpersonal and organisational skills and critical reflection upon their application.

- Reminiscence and life review undertaken with individuals, families, small groups and communities requires considerable theory building and further research.

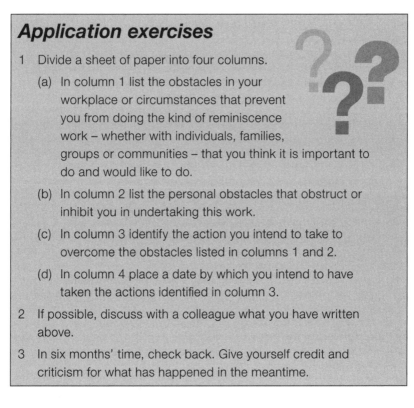

Application exercises

1 Divide a sheet of paper into four columns.

   (a) In column 1 list the obstacles in your workplace or circumstances that prevent you from doing the kind of reminiscence work – whether with individuals, families, groups or communities – that you think it is important to do and would like to do.

   (b) In column 2 list the personal obstacles that obstruct or inhibit you in undertaking this work.

   (c) In column 3 identify the action you intend to take to overcome the obstacles listed in columns 1 and 2.

   (d) In column 4 place a date by which you intend to have taken the actions identified in column 3.

2 If possible, discuss with a colleague what you have written above.

3 In six months' time, check back. Give yourself credit and criticism for what has happened in the meantime.

Further reading

Etherington K. (2004) *Becoming a Reflexive Researcher: Using ourselves in research.* London: Jessica Kingsley

Hawkins P and Shohet R. (2000) *Supervision in the Helping Professions.* Maidenhead: Open University/McGraw-Hill

Pierce TW. (2005) 'Evaluation', in BK Haight and F Gibson (Eds). *Burnside's Working with Older Adults: Group process and techniques.* Boston: Jones and Bartlett; pages 469–480

References and further reading

Age Concern. (2006) *The Age Agenda.* London: Age Concern

Aldridge D. (2000) *Music Therapy in Dementia Care.* London: Jessica Kingsley

Aldridge E. (2003) *How to be a Silver Surfer: A beginner's guide to the Internet.* London: Age Concern

Alibhai-Brown Y. (1998) *Caring for Ethnic Minority Elders: A guide.* London: Age Concern

Atkinson D. (1994) '"I got put away": group-based reminiscence with people with learning difficulties', in J Bornat (Ed). *Reminiscence Reviewed: Perspectives, evaluations and achievements.* Buckingham: Open University Press; pages 96–104

Atkinson D. (1998) 'Autobiography and learning disability', *Oral History* **26** (1): 73–80

Atkinson D (Ed). (2000) *Good Times, Bad Times: Women with learning difficulties telling their stories.* Kidderminster: Bild Publications

Atkinson D, Jackson M and Walmsley J (Eds). (1997) *Forgotten Lives: Exploring the history of learning disability.* Kidderminster: Bild Publications

Atkinson D and Williams F. (1990) *Know Me as I Am: An anthology of prose, poetry and art by people with learning difficulties.* London: Hodder and Stoughton

Baker L. (2004) 'Mixing money and memories: running an oral history business', *Oral History* **32** (1): 79–86

Barrett KG and Soltys FG. (2002) 'Geriatric social work: supporting the patient's search for meaning', *Geriatric Rehabilitation* **17** (4): 53–64

Bartlett E (Ed). (1992) *Nice Tastin': Life and food in the Caribbean.* London: Chelsea Community History Group

Bell V and Troxel D. (1997) *The Best Friends Approach to Alzheimer's Care.* Baltimore, MD: Health Professions Press

Bell V and Troxel D. (2001) *The Best Friends Staff: Building a culture of care in Alzheimer's programs.* Baltimore, MD: Health Professions Press

Bender M. (1994) 'An interesting confusion: what can we do with reminiscence groupwork?', in J Bornat (Ed). *Reminiscence Reviewed: Perspectives, evaluations and achievements.* Buckingham: Open University Press; pages 32–45

Bender M. (2005) *Therapeutic Groupwork for People with Cognitive Losses: Working with people with dementia.* Bicester: Speechmark

Bender M, Baukham P and Norris A. (1998) *The Therapeutic Purposes of Reminiscence.* London: Sage

Birren JE and Birren BA. (1996) 'Autobiography: exploring the self and encouraging development', in J Birren, G Kenyon, JE Ruth, J Schroot and T Svensson (Eds). *Aging and Biography.* New York: Springer; pages 283–299

Birren JE and Cochran K. (2001) *Telling the Stories of Life through Guided Autobiography Groups.* Baltimore, MD: Johns Hopkins University Press

Birren JE and Deutchman D. (2005) 'Guided autobiography groups', in BK Haight and F Gibson (Eds). *Burnside's Working with Older People: Group process and techniques.* Boston: Jones and Bartlett; pages 191–204

Blachman L. (2003) 'Healing through listening and legacy', in *Selected Conference Papers and Proceedings,* October 8–11, International Reminiscence and Life Review Conference, Vancouver; pages 36–38

Blackman N (Ed). (1999) *Living with Loss: Helping people with learning disabilities cope with loss and bereavement.* Brighton: Pavilion Publishing

Blackwell D. (2005) *Counselling and Psychotherapy with Refugees.* London: Jessica Kingsley

Bohlmeijer E, Smit F and Cuijpers P. (2003) 'Effects of reminiscence and life review on late-life depression: a meta-analysis', *International Journal of Geriatric Psychiatry* **18:** 1088–1094

Bond J and Cooper L. (2004) *Quality of Life and Older People.* Buckingham: Open University Press

Bornat J. (1989) 'Oral history as a social movement: reminiscence and older people', in R Perks and A Thompson (Eds). *The Oral History Reader.* London: Routledge; pages 189–205

Bornat J (Ed). (1994) *Reminiscence Reviewed: Evaluation, achievements and perspectives.* Buckingham: Open University

Bornat J. (2001) 'Reminiscence and oral history: parallel universes or shared endeavours', *Ageing and Society* **21** (2): 32–35

Brenner T and Brenner K. (2004) 'Embracing Montessori methods in dementia care', *Journal of Dementia Care* **12** (3): 24–27

Bright R. (1996) *Grief and Powerlessness: Helping people regain control of their lives.* London: Jessica Kingsley

Bright R. (1997) *Wholeness in Later Life.* London: Jessica Kingsley

Bruce E, Hodgson S and Schweitzer P. (1999) *Reminiscing with People with Dementia: A handbook for carers.* London: Age Exchange

Burns A, Dening T and Lawlor B. (2002) *Clinical Guidelines in Old Age Psychiatry.* London: Martin Dunitz

Butler R. (1963) 'The life review: an interpretation of reminiscence in the aged', *Psychiatry: Journal for the Study of Interpersonal Processes* **6** (1): 65–76

Butler R. (1995) 'The life review', in BK Haight and JD Webster (Eds). *The Art and Science of Reminiscing: Theory, research, methods and applications.* Washington, DC: Taylor and Francis; pages xvii–xxi

Butler SJ. (2004) *Hearing and Sight Loss: A handbook for professional carers.* London: Age Concern

Cappeliez P. (2002) 'Cognitive-reminiscence therapy for depressed older adults in day hospital and long term care', in JD Webster and BK Haight (Eds). *Critical Advances in Reminiscence Work: From theory to application.* Boston: Jones and Bartlett; pages 300–313

Cappeliez P and O'Rourke N. (2002) 'Personality traits and existential concerns as predictors of the functions of reminiscence in older adults', *Journal of Gerontology* **57:** 116–123

Cappeliez P, Lavallee and O'Rourke N. (2001) 'Functions of reminiscence in later life as viewed by young and old adults', *Canadian Journal on Aging* **20:** 577–589

Cappeliez P, O'Rourke N and Chaudhury H. (2005) 'The functions of reminiscence and mental health in later life', *Aging and Mental Health* **9** (4): 295-301

Carnwell R and Buchanan J (Eds). (2004) *Effective Practice in Health and Social Care: A partnership approach.* Maidenhead: Open University/McGraw-Hill

Cheston R and Bender M. (1999) *Understanding Dementia: The man with the worried eyes.* London: Jessica Kingsley

Clair AA. (1996) *Therapeutic Uses of Music with Older Adults.* Baltimore, MD: Health Professions Press

Clare L. (2005) 'Cognitive rehabilitation for people with dementia', in M Marshall (Ed). *Perspectives on Rehabilitation and Dementia.* London: Jessica Kingsley; pages 180–186

Clare L, Woods RT, Moniz Cook ED, Orrell M and Spector A. (2003) 'Cognitive rehabilitation interventions to improve memory functioning in early-stage Alzheimer's disease and vascular dementia', *Cochrane Database of Systematic Reviews,* 2. Oxford: Wiley Interscience

Coleman PG. (1986) *Ageing and Reminiscence Processes.* Chichester: Wiley

Coleman PG and O'Hanlon A. (2004) *Ageing and Development: Theories and research.* London: Hodder Arnold

Cooper M. (2005) 'Mabel Cooper – self advocate', *Oral History* **33** (1): 36

Craig C. (2005) *Meaningful Making: A practice guide for occupational therapy staff.* Stirling: Dementia Services Development Centre

Crimmens P. (1997) *Storymaking and Creative Groupwork with Older People.* London: Jessica Kingsley

de Klerk-Rubin V. (1994) 'How validation is misunderstood', *Journal of Dementia Care* **2** (2): 14–16

de Klerk-Rubin V. (1995) 'A safe and friendly place to share feelings', *Journal of Dementia Care* **3** (3): 22–24

Denis P and Makiwane N. (2003) 'Stories of love, pain and courage: AIDS orphans and memory boxes', *Oral History* **31** (2): 66–74

Dobrof R. (1984) 'Introduction: a time for re-claiming the past', in M Kaminsky (Ed). *The Uses of Reminiscence: New ways of working with older adults.* London: Haworth; pages xvii–xviii

Doel M and Sawdon C. (1999) *The Essential Groupworker.* London: Jessica Kingsley

Doka KJ. (2002) *Disenfranchised Grief: New directions, challenges and strategies for practice.* Champaign, IL: Research Press

Down's Syndrome Association. (2004) *Ageing and its Consequences for People with Down's Syndrome: A guide for parents and carers.* London: Down's Syndrome Association

Elford H, Wilson F, McKee KJ, Chung MC, Bolton G and Goudie F. (2005) 'Psychological benefits of solitary reminiscence writing: an exploratory study', *Aging and Mental Health* **9** (4): 305–314

Erikson EH. (1982) *The Life Cycle Completed.* New York: WW Norton

Etherington K. (2004) *Becoming a Reflexive Researcher: Using ourselves in research.* London: Jessica Kingsley

Feil N. (2002) *The Validation Breakthrough: Simple techniques for communicating with people with Alzheimer's-type dementia.* Baltimore, MD: Health Professions Press

Fleming R (Ed). (2001) *Challenge Depression: A manual to help staff identify and reduce depression in aged care facilities.* Canberra: Commonwealth Department of Health and Ageing

Fry PS. (1995) 'A conceptual model of socialisation and agentic trait factors that mediate the development of reminiscence styles and their health outcomes', in BK Haight and JD Webster (Eds). *The Art and Science of Reminiscing: Theory, research, methods and applications.* Washington, DC: Taylor and Francis; pages 49–60

Gibson F. (2000) *The Reminiscence Trainer's Pack.* London: Age Concern

Gibson F. (2004) *The Past in the Present: Using reminiscence in health and social care.* Baltimore, MD: Health Professions Press

Godfrey M and Denby T. (2005) *Depression and Older People.* Bristol: Policy Press

Golden S and Perlstein S. (2004) *Legacy Works: Transforming memory into visual art.* New York: Elders Share the Arts

Goldsmith M. (1996) *Hearing the Voice of People with Dementia: Opportunities and obstacles.* London: Jessica Kingsley

Grudzen M and Soltys FG. (2000) 'Reminiscence at end of life: a living legacy', *Dimensions* **7** (3): 4–8

Haight BK. (1998) 'Use of life review and life story books in families with Alzheimer's disease', in P Schweitzer (Ed). *Reminiscence in Dementia Care.* London: Age Exchange; pages 85–90

Haight BK, Coleman P and Lord K. (1995) 'The linchpins of a successful life review: structure, evaluation and individuality', in BK Haight and JD Webster (Eds). *The Art and Science of Reminiscence: Theory, research, methods and applications.* Washington, DC: Taylor and Francis; pages 179–192

Haight BK and Gibson F (Eds). (2005) *Burnside's Working with Older People: Group process and techniques.* Boston: Jones and Bartlett

Haight BK and Gibson F. (2006) 'The Northern Ireland life review/life storybook project for people with dementia', *Alzheimer's and Dementia* in press.

Haight BK, Michel Y and Hendrix S. (2000) 'The extended effects of the life review in nursing home residents', *International Journal of Aging and Human Development* **50** (2): 151–168

Haight BK and Webster JD (Eds). (1995) *The Art and Science of Reminiscence: Theory, research, methods and applications.* Washington, DC: Taylor and Francis

Harris J. (2005) 'Speech and language therapy', in M Marshall (Ed). *Perspectives on Rehabilitation and Dementia.* London: Jessica Kingsley; pages 121–127

Hawkins P and Shohet R. (2000) *Supervision in the Helping Professions.* Maidenhead: Open University/McGraw-Hill

Help the Aged Education Department. (1981) *Recall.* London: Help the Aged

Hendricks J (Ed). (1995) *The Meaning of Reminiscence and Life Review.* New York: Baywood Publishing

Henley A and Schott J. (2004) *Culture, Religion and Patient Care in a Multi-ethnic Society: A handbook for professionals.* London: Age Concern

Hewitt H. (2000) 'A life story approach for people with profound learning disabilities', *British Journal of Nursing* **9** (2): 90–95

Hewitt H. (2003) 'Life story books for people with learning disability', *Learning Disability Practice* **6** (8): 18–22

Hopkins G. (2002) 'This is your life', *Community Care* 7–13 March (1412): 40

Hubbard G, Cook A, Tester S and Downs M. (2002) 'Beyond words: older people with dementia using and interpreting nonverbal behaviour', *Journal of Aging Studies* **16:** 155–167

Hunt L, Marshall M and Rowlings C (Eds). (1997) *Past Trauma in Late Life.* London: Jessica Kingsley

Janicki MP and Dalton AJ. (1999) *Dementia, Aging and Intellectual Disabilities: A handbook.* Philadelphia, PA: Brunner/Mazel

Jenkins C and Merry J. (2005) *Relative Grief.* London: Jessica Kingsley

Jones C, Lyons C and Cunningham C. (2003) 'Life review following critical illness in young men', *Nursing in Critical Care* **8** (6): 256–263

Jones GM and Miesen B. (2004) *Care-giving in Dementia: Research and applications*, 3. Hove: Brunner-Routledge

Kemp M. (1978) *Audio-visual Reminiscence Aids for Elderly People, including the Mentally Frail.* London: Department of Health and Social Security

Kerr D. (1997) *Down's Syndrome and Dementia: A practitioner's guide.* Birmingham: Venture Press

Killick J. (1994) 'There's so much more to hear when you stop and listen to individual voices', *Journal of Dementia Care* **2** (5): 16–17

Killick J. (1997) *You are Words: Dementia poems.* London: Hawker

Killick J. (2005) 'Conversation', *Journal of Dementia Care Calendar*

Killick J and Allan K. (2001) *Communication and the Care of People with Dementia.* Buckingham: Open University Press

Kitwood T. (1997) *Dementia Reconsidered.* Buckingham: Open University Press

Kurokawa Y. (1998) 'Couple reminiscence with Japanese dementia patients and their spouses', in P Schweitzer (Ed). *Reminiscence in Dementia Care.* London: Age Exchange; pages 108–112

Lynn LE. (2001) 'A shadow over this day', *Social Service Administration Magazine* (Chicago: University of Chicago Press)

McConkey J. (1997) *The Anatomy of Memory: An anthology.* Oxford: Oxford University Press

McCrea JM and Smith TB. (1997) 'Types and models of intergenerational programs', in S Newman et al (Eds). *Intergenerational Programs: Past, present and future.* Washington, DC: Taylor and Francis; pages 81–93

McKee K, Wilson F, Elford H et al. (2003) *Evaluating the Impact of Reminiscence on the Quality of Life of Older People.* ESRC Report. Sheffield: University of Sheffield

MacKinlay E. (2001) *The Spiritual Dimension of Ageing.* London: Jessica Kingsley

Mandelstam M. (2005) *Community Care Practice and the Law.* London: Jessica Kingsley

Mansfield J. (2005) *Effective Communication with People who have Hearing Difficulties.* Bicester: Speechmark

Manthorpe J and Iliffe S. (2005) *Depression and Later Life.* London: Jessica Kingsley

Marshall M. (1997) *State of the Art in Dementia Care.* London: Centre for Policy on Ageing

Marshall M. (1998) 'How it helps to see dementia as a disability', *Journal of Dementia Care* **6** (1): 15–17

Mistry T and Brown A. (1991) 'Black/white co-working in groups', *Groupwork* **4** (2): 101–118

Mistry T and Brown A (Eds). (1997) *Race and Groupwork.* London: Whiting and Birch

Northen H and Kurland R. (2001) *Social Work with Groups.* New York: Columbia University Press

Nuttall S and Coetzee C (Eds). (1998) *The Making of History in South Africa.* Oxford: Oxford University Press

Osborn C. (1993) *The Reminiscence Handbook: Ideas for creative activities with older people.* London: Age Exchange

Parkes CM. (1986) *Bereavement: Studies of grief in later life.* London: Penguin

Parr S, Duchan J and Pound C. (2003) *Aphasia Inside Out: Reflections on communication disability.* Maidenhead: Open University

Pear T. (1922) *Remembering and Forgetting.* London: Methuen

Perlstein S and Bliss J. (2003) *Generating Community: Intergenerational partnerships through the expressive arts.* New York: Elders Share the Arts

Perrin T and May H. (2000) *Wellbeing in Dementia: An occupational approach for therapists and carers.* London: Churchill Livingstone

Pickles W. (2005) 'Kitwood reconsidered: dementia, personhood and music', *Generations Review* **15** (1): 25–27

Pierce TW. (2003) 'The use of multimedia to compile life history materials', in *Selected Conference Papers and Proceedings,* October 8–11, International Reminiscence and Life Review Conference, Vancouver; pages 91–102

Pierce TW. (2005) 'Evaluation issues in group work', in BK Haight and F Gibson (Eds). *Burnside's Working with Older Adults: Group process and techniques.* Boston: Jones and Bartlett; pages 469–480

Popple K. (1995) *Analysing Community Work: Its theory and practice.* Maidenhead: Open University

Popple K, Quinney A and Jeffs T. (2005) *An Introduction to Community: An interdisciplinary guide to policy and practice.* Maidenhead: Open University/McGraw-Hill

Rainbow A. (2003) *The Reminiscence Skills Training Handbook.* Bicester: Speechmark

Read P. (1996) *Returning to Nothing: The meaning of lost places.* Cambridge: Cambridge University Press

Rubin DC (Ed). (1996) *Remembering our Past: Studies in autobiographical memory.* Cambridge: Cambridge University Press

Sampson F. (2004) *Creative Writing in Health and Social Care.* London: Jessica Kingsley

Savill D. (2002) *A Time to Share: Powerful personal stories for teaching history and citizenship.* London: Age Exchange

Schweitzer P. (1993) *Reminiscence Projects for Children and Older People.* London: Age Exchange

Schweitzer P (Ed). (1995) *Making Memories Matter: Reminiscence and inter-generational activities.* London: Age Exchange and European Reminiscence Network

Schweitzer P (Ed). (1998a) *The Journey of a Lifetime.* London: Age Exchange and European Reminiscence Network

Schweitzer P (Ed). (1998b) *Reminiscence in Dementia Care.* London: Age Exchange and European Reminiscence Network

Schweitzer P (Ed). (2004) *Mapping Memories: Reminiscence with ethnic minority elders.* London: Age Exchange

Sherman E. (1991) 'Reminiscentia: cherished objects as memorabilia in late-life reminiscence', *International Journal of Aging and Human Development* **38:** 89–100.

Sherman J. (2004) *Getting the Most from your Computer: A practical guide for older home users.* London: Age Concern

Shulman L. (1999) *The Skills of Helping Individuals, Families, Groups and Communities.* Itasca, IL: Peacock

Sim R. (1997) *Social and Creative Activities with Older People in Care.* Bicester: Winslow Press

Spector A, Orrell M, Davies S and Woods RT. (1998) 'Reality orientation for dementia: a review of the evidence of effectiveness', *Cochrane Database of Systematic Reviews,* 4. Oxford: Wiley Interscience

Stelson C and Dauk-Bleess R. (2003) 'Lasting memories: an intergenerational writing project in the elementary classroom with implications for reminiscence and life review work with elders', *Selected Conference Papers and Proceedings,* October 8–11, International Reminiscence and Life Review Conference, Vancouver; pages 40–45

Stuart M. (1997) *Looking Back, Looking Forward: Reminiscence with people with learning disability.* Brighton: Pavilion Publishing

Taulbee LR and Folson JC. (1966) 'Reality orientation for geriatric patients', *Hospital and Community Psychiatry* **17:** 133–135

Taylor-Goh S (Ed). (2005) *Clinical Guidelines.* Bicester: Royal College of Speech and Language Therapists/Speechmark

Thompson P. (2000) *The Voice of the Past: Oral history.* Oxford: Oxford University Press

Thomson A. (1998) 'Anzac memories: putting popular memory theory into practice in Australia', in R Perks and A Thomson (Eds). *The Oral History Reader.* London: Routledge; pages 300–310

Thorgrimsen L, Kennedy L, Douglas C, Garcia C and Bender M. (2002) 'The group activity form', *Journal of Occupational Therapy* **65** (6): 283–287

Tuckman BW. (1965) 'Developmental sequence in small groups', *Psychological Bulletin* **63:** 384–399

Van Dongen E. (2005) 'Remembering in times of misery: can older people in South Africa "get through"?' *Ageing and Society* **25** (4): 525–541

Watt LM and Cappeliez P. (1995) 'Reminiscence interventions for the treatment of depression in older adults', in BK Haight and JD Webster (Eds). *The Art and Science of Reminiscing: Theory, research, methods and applications.* Washington, DC, DC: Taylor and Francis; pages 221–232

Watt L and Wong P. (1990) 'A taxonomy of reminiscence and therapeutic implications', *Journal of Gerontological Social Work* **16:** 37–57

Webster JD. (1997) 'The reminiscence functions scale: a replication', *International Journal of Aging and Human Development* **44** (2): 137–149

Webster JD and Haight BK (Eds). (2002) *Critical Advances in Reminiscence Work: From theory to application.* New York: Springer-Verlag

Webster JD and McCall ME. (1999) 'Reminiscence functions across adulthood: a replication and extension', *Journal of Adult Development* **6:** 73–85

Wilkinson H, Kerr D, Cunningham C and Rae C. (2004) *Home for Good?* Brighton: Pavilion/Joseph Rowntree

Wong PT and Watt LM. (1991) 'What types of reminiscence are associated with successful ageing?', *Journal of Psychology and Ageing* **6** (2): 272–279

Woods RT. (2004) 'Review: reminiscence and life review are effective therapies for depression in the elderly', *Evidence-based Mental Health* **7:** 81–83

Woods RT, Spector A, Jones C, Orrell M and Davies S. (2005) 'Reminiscence therapy for dementia: a review of the evidence for its effectiveness', *Cochrane Database of Systematic Reviews,* 2. Oxford: Wiley Interscience

Yow V. (1994) *Reconsidering Oral History: A practical guide for social scientists.* New York: Sage

Appendix 1 **Recording forms**

This section gives examples of forms that you can use or adapt to keep a record of your reminiscence work with individuals, couples and groups.

Form 1, Personal History (pages 268–269), summarises background information for each individual. If possible, much of this information should be obtained during an initial interview if you are planning to undertake groupwork. If you are working with an individual, it could be used as a preliminary introduction, as a guide for a number of sessions or to gather information for a life story book.

Form 2, Individual Summary Record (page 270), may be used either in individual or in group sessions to summarise the response of each participant in each session. Complete it after each session by rating participants' responses on a scale of 0–4.

Form 3, Reminiscence Group – Group Sessional Record (page 271), summarises the response of all members at each session and records attendance. Complete it after each session.

Form 4, Reminiscence Group – Leader's Sessional Record (page 272), refers to the content and process of each session. It also includes notes on debriefing and supervision meetings. If you are co-working, this form is best completed jointly by the leaders as soon as possible after each session.

Form 5, Group Activity Form (pages 273–275), is an alternative to Form 4 (page 272) for use with a group of people with dementia.

Form 6, Clearance Form – Consent Form (page 276). It is important to have written consent from each participant if there is any likelihood that contributions may be used publicly.

The Quick Reference Age Grid is on page 61.

1 Personal history

Name		
Date of birth		Place of birth
Source of information		
History compiled by		Date
Preferred language		How person likes to be addressed
First language		Country of origin
Present marital status		Maiden name
Date married	Place married	Spouse/partner's name
Date bereaved		
Number of children	Number of grandchildren	Number of great grandchildren
Names (ages) of children:		Spouses/partners
Grandchildren		Grandchildren's spouses/partners
Own mother's maiden name		Father's name
Own brothers/sisters		Spouses/partners of brothers/sisters
Close friends and relatives		

Schools attended: Primary	Secondary		Other
Employment: 1		3	
2		4	
Significant places		Length of time spent there	
Reasons why significant			
Achievements or awards			
Significantl events in life			
Religion	Church/mosque/temple/ synagogue attended		
Personal values			
Hobbies and interests			
Favourite pets			
Musical preferences at different times throughout life			
Particular likes		Particular dislikes	
Special medical conditions (eg diabetes, allergies)			
Sensory impairments		Best method of communication	
Dietary restrictions/preferences			
Additional information			

2 Individual summary record

Participant's name				Date					
Individual session	Group session	Activity							
Sessions		1	2	3	4	5	6	7	8
Willingness to join session									
0 Refused to join session									
1 Needed persuading									
2 Needed reminding									
3 Came along without prompting									
Memory									
0 No recall									
1 Recalled odd incidents									
2 Good recall without prompting									
3 Memory intact									
Interaction (spontaneity)									
0 Disruptive									
1 Offered nothing at all									
2 Spoke only if asked									
3 Responded to other participants									
4 Initiated interaction									
Participation/responsiveness (need not be verbal)									
0 No response									
1 Little response/uncooperative									
2 Active participation when prompted									
3 Active participation without prompting									
Enjoyment									
0 Showed no signs of enjoyment									
1 Occasionally showed pleasure									
2 Enjoyed majority of session									
3 Thoroughly enjoyed session									
Comments									

3 Reminiscence group – group sessional record

Staff		Activity			Date	
Members' names	Attend-ance ✓ Absence ✗	Willing-ness to join group	Memory	Inter-action	Partici-pation	Enjoy-ment
1						
2						
3						
4						
5						
6						
7						
8						
9						
10						

Main topics discussed/material used

Themes

Comments

Suggestions

4 Reminiscence group – leader(s)' sessional record

Session no.	Date/time of session

Group leaders

Group members	Reasons for absences, if any

Changes since last session

Outline of session

Theme	Topics covered

Group activity and process

Notes on individuals

Interaction between group leaders

Overall assessment of session

Comments/suggestions

Debriefing after session

Supervision

5 Group activity form for people with dementia

Group	Session	Date
Leader(s):		
Comments		

Group members	Note absentees and reason
A	
B	
C	
D	

	A	B	C	D
1 Willingness to join group				
0 Too ill (i) or absent (a)				
1 Refused to join group				
2 Needed persuading				
3 Needed reminding				
4 Came along without prompting				
2 Confusion/inappropriate contributions (Rating based on answering appropriately. The number of comments is irrelevant; rate only the content.)				
0 Did not contribute anything or all contributions inappropriate				
1 Almost all contributions confused/inappropriate				
2 Some contributions inappropriate				
3 Most contributions appropriate				
4 All contributions appropriate				

Form 5 *continued*

	A	B	C	D
3 Energy level				
0 Doziness frequent				
1 Persistent restlessness				
2 Intermittent doziness				
3 Intermittent restlessness				
4 Appeared appropriately calm				
4 Type of reminiscence (Positive/negative/neutral = emotion expressed by member while recalling the event, not content's emotion. Member must elaborate the memory in order to be scored as 'reminiscing'. 'Yes'/'No' answers to prompts score as 'No reminiscence'.)				
0 No reminiscence				
1 Recalled neutral-toned events				
2 Recalled positive-toned events				
3 Recalled negative-toned events				
4 Recalled positive and negative events				
Comments				

	A	B	C	D
5 Interaction/relationships (Tick all appropriate boxes)				
0a Rude/inconsiderate				
0b Monopolised the session				
0c Disruptive				
0d Said nothing				

5   Interaction/relationships *continued*

1	Spoke only to leaders or to members when prompted			
2a	Made spontaneous comments to no one in particular			
2b	Made spontaneous comments to staff			
2c	Made spontaneous comments to one other member			
2d	Made spontaneous comments to other members			
3	Helped others take part			
6	**Interest/participation in the group** (need not be verbal) (Tick all appropriate boxes)			
0	Little response/uncooperative			
1	Active participation when prompted			
2	Active participation without prompting some of the time			
3	Active participation without prompting most of the time			
4	Active participation without prompting all of the time			
7	**Enjoyment/satisfaction**			
0	Showed no signs of enjoyment/satisfaction			
1	Occasionally showed pleasure/satisfaction			
2	Showed some enjoyment/satisfaction most of the time			
3	Enjoyed/satisfied with majority of sessions			
4	Thoroughly enjoyed/satisfied with session			

Source: Thorgrimsen and colleagues (2002)

continued

6 Clearance form

Your contribution of		
will form part of the collection of material relating to the past and present. This form has been drawn up in order to ensure that we use your contribution only in accordance with your wishes.		
1 May we use your contribution:		
a for public reference?	Yes	No
b for research purposes?	Yes	No
c for educational use (in seminars, workshops, schools, colleges, universities)?	Yes	No
d for broadcasting purposes (radio or TV)?	Yes	No
e as a source of information that may be published?	Yes	No
f in a public performance, display or exhibition?	Yes	No
2 May we mention your name?	Yes	No
3 Are there any further restrictions you wish to place on this material? (please specify)		

Signature of interviewee	Date
Signature of principal family carer (if appropriate)	Date
Signature of professional carer	Date
Signature of interviewer	Date

Appendix 2 **Resource agencies**

Note: numbers that begin 080 are free to the caller; numbers that begin 0845 are charged at local call rate; numbers that begin 087 are charged at special service higher rate

Age Concern Training
Martindale
Hawks Green Lane
Cannock WS11 7XN
Tel: 01543 503660
Fax: 01543 504640, 0800 328 0894
Website: www.ageconcern.org.uk
In-house training service and short courses at various locations throughout England, including one-day reminiscence courses.

Age Exchange Reminiscence Centre
11 Blackheath Village
London SE3 9LA
Tel: 020 8318 9105
Fax: 020 8318 0060
Email: administrator@age-exchange.org.uk
Website: www.age-exchange.org.uk
Museum, shop, café, exhibitions, theatre, reminiscence sessions, boxes of artefacts for hire, inter-generational work, conferences and training workshops.
Provides training and project support throughout England.
Publishes reminiscence books, Reminiscence Exchange *and trigger materials.*

Alzheimer's Forum
Website:
www.alzheimersforum.org
A small group of people with dementia maintains a website to share personal experiences, exchange views and learn from each other. Contributions are invited.

Alzheimer's Society
Gordon House
10 Greencoat Place
London SW1P 1PH
Tel: 020 7306 0606
Helpline: 0845 300 0336
(8.30am–6.30pm, Mon–Fri)
Fax: 020 7306 0808
Email:
enquiries@alzheimers.org.uk
Website: www.alzheimers.org.uk
Service provision, carers' support groups, information and education for carers and professionals, campaigning, advocacy, research and publications.

British Association for Local History

PO Box 6549
Somersal Herbert
Ashbourne DE6 5WH
Tel: 01283 585947
Website: www.balh.co.uk
A national charity that promotes the study of local history. Publishes books, pamphlets, The Local Historian *and* Local History News *and organises guided visits to major repositories, libraries, historical sites and museums.*

British Library Sound Archive

see Oral History/National Life Story Collection

Care Council for Wales

7th Floor
South Gate House
Wood Street
Cardiff CF10 1EW
Tel: 029 2022 6257
Fax: 029 2038 4764
Email: info@ccwales.org.uk
Website: www.ccwales.org.uk
Social care workforce regulator for Wales concerned with good practice, conduct, education, training and registration.

Commanet

PO Box 27
Leeds LS13 1XS
Tel: 0845 45 88 132
Email: info@commanet.org
Website: www.commanet.org
Promotes the collection and archiving of still and video images, text and oral narratives using Comma software. The archives are searchable databases of community and group cultural heritage that are published locally as CD-ROMs and on the Internet.

Commission for Racial Equality

St Dunstan's House
201–211 Borough High Street
London SE1 1GZ
Tel: 020 7939 0000
Fax: 020 7939 0004
Website: www.cre.gov.uk
Works to reduce discrimination and promote equality.

Disabled Living Foundation

380–384 Harrow Road
London W9 2HU
Tel: 020 7289 6111
Helpline: 0845 130 9177
(10am–4pm, Mon–Fri)
Textphone: 020 7432 8009
Website: www.dlf.org.uk
Assists older and disabled people to locate equipment solutions that enable them to live more independently. Provides information, advice, factsheets and demonstrations of assistive technology and equipment.

Edinburgh People's Story Museum

Canongate Tolbooth
163 Canongate
Royal Mile
Edinburgh EH8 8BN
Tel: 0131 529 4057
Fax: 0131 556 3439
Website: www.cac.uk/edinburgh/people_story.htm
Collects local history and provides exhibitions on the lives, work and leisure of Edinburgh people, from the late 18th century to the present day.

European Reminiscence Network

c/o Pam Schweitzer
15 Camden Row
Blackheath
London SE3 OQA
Tel: 020 8852 9293
Email: schweitzer@beeb.net
Website: www.europeanreminiscence-network.org
Aims to increase the profile of reminiscence, encourage best practice, exchange skills and raise the profile of reminiscence across Europe and beyond. Conferences, festivals, training programmes, publications and collaborative research projects with trans-European partners.

General Social Care Council

Goldings House
2 Hay's Lane
London SE1 2HB
Tel: 020 7397 5100
Information line: 020 7397 5800
(10am–noon, 2pm–4pm, Mon–Fri)
Fax: 020 7397 5101
Email: info@gscc.org.uk
Website: www.gscc.org.uk
Social care workforce regulator for England, concerned with good practice, conduct, education, training and registration.

Help the Aged

207–221 Pentonville Road
London N1 9UZ
Tel: 020 7278 1114
Fax: 020 7278 1116
Email: info@helptheaged.org.uk
Website: www.helptheaged.org.uk
Publisher of Recall *(out of print but available through libraries and social agencies).*
Advocacy and campaigning on issues of concern to older people, including elder abuse.

History Talk
240B Lancaster Road
London W11 4AH
Tel: 020 7792 2282
Fax: 020 7792 4426
Email: info@historytalk.org
Website: www.historytalk.org
Memories groups, reminiscence training, inter-generational work in schools, music and drama reminiscence sessions with people with early memory loss/ dementia, projects, exhibitions, publications, support of reminiscence volunteers working with housebound older people. Working with groups of minority ethnic elders to record and publish their stories.

Imperial War Museum
Lambeth Road
London SE1 6HZ
Tel: 020 7416 5320/5321
Fax: 020 7416 5374
Website: www.iwm.org.uk
Sound archive, exhibitions, publications, oral accounts of wartime experience and Holocaust records.

Imperial War Museum North
The Quays
Trafford Wharf
Trafford Park
Manchester M17 1TZ
Tel: 0161 836 4000
Fax: 0161 836 4012
See also Imperial War Museum

International Institute for Reminiscence and Life Review
Center for Continuing Education/ Extension
University of Wisconsin-Superior
Belknap & Catlin Avenue
PO Box 2000
Old Main 102
Superior, WI 54880-4500, USA
Tel: +715 394 8469
Email: j.kunz@uwsuper.edu
Website: www. reminiscenceandlifereview.org
A North American-based network of reminiscence practitioners and researchers. Holds biennial conferences.

Journal of Dementia Care
Hawker Publications
Culvert House
Culvert Road
London SW11 5DH
Tel: 020 7720 2108
Fax: 020 7498 3023
Email: suec@hawkerpublications. com
Website: www.careinfo.org
Multi-professional publication with six issues a year.

Living Archive
Old Bath House
205 Stratford Road
Wolverton
Milton Keynes MK12 5RL
Tel: 01908 322568
Fax: 01908 312974
Website: www.livingarchive.org.uk
A creative cultural and community development agency. Publications, arts projects, local archive, reminiscence and older people's theatre group.

Mothers' Living Stories Project

Website: www.
motherslivingstories.org
*A project (based in San Francisco)
to help mothers with life-
threatening or chronic illness to
review their lives and to record
their stories as legacies for their
children.*

Museums Reminiscence Network and Directory

c/o Steph Mastoris
Snibston Discovery Park
Ashby Road
Coalville LE6 3LN
Tel: 01530 278444
Fax: 01530 813301
Email: smastoris@leics.gov.uk
*Lists museums throughout the UK
that run special projects with older
people and have collections that
may be used by agencies working
with older people.*

National Extension College

Michael Young Centre
Purbeck Road
Cambridge CB2 2HN
Tel: 01223 400200
Fax: 01223 400399
Email: info@nec.ac.uk
Website: www.nec.ac.uk
*Publisher and distributor of open/
distance learning materials.*

National Center for Creative Aging

c/o Elders Share the Arts
138 South Oxford Street
Brookly, NY 1127
USA
Tel: +001 718 398 3870
Email: ncca@creativeaging.org
*Projects and publications that
transform memories into art.
Produces an e-newsletter.*

National Network for the Arts in Health

The Menier Chocolate Factory
51 Southwark Street
London SE1 1RU
Tel: 0870 9143 4555
Website: www.nnah.org.uk
*Provides information and services
for organisations and individuals
concerning health-related arts
projects, funding, news and
events throughout the UK.*

National Open College Network

9 St James Court
Friar Gate
Derby DE1 1BT
Tel: 01332 268080
Fax: 01332 268081
Website: www.nocn.org.uk
*The central organisation for
11 Open College Networks in the
9 regions of England, Wales and
Northern Ireland.*

Northern Ireland Film and Television Commission

Digital Film Archive
21 Alfred Street
Belfast BT2 8ED
Tel: 028 9023 2444
Fax: 028 9023 9918
Website: www.niftc.co.uk
www.digitalfilmarchive.net
Digital photographic archive of life in Northern Ireland 1897–2000, available for public viewing at Armagh, Belfast, Coleraine, Cultra, Londonderry and Omagh. Staff will visit to enable reminiscence groups to view and discuss the archive.

Northern Ireland Reminiscence Network

23 Scolban Road
Dromore BT25 8DH
Tel: 028 9269 9859
Seeks to value people of all ages by valuing their memories and to promote good reminiscence practice. Provides a newsletter and reminiscence training, and undertakes reminiscence developmental projects in conjunction with health and social services, museums and library partners.

Northern Ireland Social Care Council

7th Floor, Millennium House
19–25 Great Victoria Street
Belfast BT2 7AQ
Tel: 028 9041 7600
Fax: 028 9041 7601
Email: info@niscc.n-i.nhs.uk
Website: www.niscc.info

Social care workforce regulator for Northern Ireland concerned with good practice, conduct, education, training and registration.

Open University

Information Officer
School of Health and Social Care
Open University
Walton Hall
Milton Keynes MK7 6AA
Tel: 0870 333 4340
Website: www.open.ac.uk
For information about the OU's distance learning courses and publications in health and social care.

Oral History/National Life Story Collection

British Library Sound Archive
96 Euston Road
London NW1 2DB
Tel: 020 7412 7404
Fax: 020 7412 7441
Email: nsa-nlsc@bl.uk
website: www.bl.uk/collections/sound-archive/nlsc.html
Undertakes oral history fieldwork projects and advises on methods of recording. Provides training days, public talks and seminars, public listening and viewing services in London and Yorkshire, reference library and on-line catalogue of oral history holdings.

Oral History Society
c/o Department of History
Essex University
Colchester CO4 3SQ
Tel: 020 7412 7405
Website: www.oralhistory.org.uk
*Promotes the development of
oral history, and provides training
workshops, conferences and
publications including the journal*
Oral History.

Pabulum
217 Silver Road
Norwich NR3 4TL
Tel: 01603 424100
Email: pabulum.norfolk@virgin.net
*A Norfolk-based charity. Works
with reminiscence-trained
volunteers who offer domiciliary
reminiscence and other creative
activity sessions for people with
dementia still living at home.*

**Policy Research Institute on
Ageing and Ethnicity**
31–32 Park Row
Leeds L51 5JD
Tel: 0113 285 5990
Fax: 0113 285 5999
Email: info@priae.org
Website: www.priae.org
*Charity working to improve quality
of life for black and minority
ethnic older people in the UK
and Europe. Aims to increase
good practice through policy,
research, information, training and
consultancy.*

**Practice Development Unit
(MHSOP)**
Whitchurch Hospital
Park Road
Cardiff CF14 7BP
Tel: 029 2033 6073
Email: pdu@cardiffandvale.wales.
nhs.uk
Website: www.signpostjournal.
co.uk
*Library of reminiscence materials,
publishes* Signpost *and
information for those working
with and caring for people with
dementia and older people with
mental health needs in South
Glamorgan. South Wales base
of the Dementia Development
Services Centre Wales.*

**Rafe Project (Reminiscence
Approaches with the Frail
Elderly)**
Shirehall House
Market Avenue
Norwich NR1 3JQ
Tel: 01603 663942
Email: margaret.plummer@norfolk.
gov.uk
*Reminiscence, exercise, crafts
and aromatherapy/gentle massage
for older people in residential
and community venues, and for
people with dementia, and training
for their carers. Development
of reminiscence rooms and
community archiving groups.*

Refugee Council
240–250 Ferndale Road
London SW9 8BB
Tel: 020 7346 6700
Fax: 020 7346 6701
Website: www.refugeecouncil.
org.uk
*Offers advice, and translated
information and can provide
information about locally based
refugee organisations.*

**Royal National Institute of the
Blind (RNIB)**
105 Judd Street
London WC1H 9NE
Tel: 020 7388 1266
Helpline: 0845 766 9999
(9am–5pm, Mon–Fri)
Fax: 020 7388 2034
Website: www.rnib.org.uk
*Information and advice, resources
and publications.*

**Royal National Institute for
Deaf People (RNID)**
19–23 Featherstone Street
London EC1Y 8SL
Tel: 0808 808 0123
Textphone: 0808 808 9000
Fax: 020 7296 8199
Email: informationline@rnid.org.uk
Website: www.rnid.org.uk
*Information and advice, resources
and publications.*

**Scottish Social Services
Council**
Compass House
Discovery Quay
11 Riverside Drive
Dundee DD1 4NY
Tel: 01382 207101
Information line: 0845 603 0891
Fax: 01382 207215
Email: enquiries@sssc.uk.com
Website: www.sssc.uk.com
*Social care workforce regulator for
Scotland, concerned with good
practice, conduct, education,
training and registration.*

Sense
11–13 Clifton Terrace
London N4 3SR
Tel: 020 7272 7774
Textphone: 020 7272 9648
Fax: 020 7272 6012
Email: info@sense.org.uk
Website: www.sense.org.uk
*A national organisation for
deafblind people, offering advice,
information, self-help groups and
a wide range of support services
such as communication guides
and training.*

Sense Scotland
43 Middlesex Street
Kinning Park
Glasgow G41 1EE
Tel: 0141 429 0294
Textphone: 0141 418 7170
Fax: 0141 429 0295
Email: info@sensescotland.org.uk
Website: www.sensescotland.org.uk
A national organisation for deafblind people, offering advice, information, self-help groups and a wide range of support services such as communication guides and training.

SHAP Working Party on World Religions in Education
PO Box 38580
London SW1P 3XF
Tel: 020 7898 1494
Fax: 020 7898 1493
Website: www.shap.org.uk
Promotes study of world religions at all educational levels through publishing and discussion. Produces annually a calendar of religious festivals in twelve major world religions together with a wall planner and booklet describing each festival.

Sonas aPc
St Mary's
185–203 Merrion Road
Dublin 4, Ireland
Tel: +353 1 260 8138
Fax: +353 1 219 5937
Email: sonasapc@iol.ie
Website: www.sonasapc.ie
Training programmes, newsletters and workshop materials to activate potential in older people with dementia and people with learning disabilities, using sensory stimulation such as music, touch, fragrance, taste and vision.

Sound Sense
7 Tavern Street
Stowmarket
Suffolk IP14 1PJ
Tel: 01449 673990
Fax: 01449 673994
Email: info@soundsense.org
Website: www.soundsense.org
Advice and information service on music and disability. Publishes the quarterly journal, Sounding Board.

Speechmark
Telford Road
Bicester
Oxfordshire OX26 4LQ
Tel: 01869 244644
Fax: 01869 320040
Email: info@speechmark.net
Website: www.speechmark.net
Publisher and distributor of reminiscence books and materials. Formerly called Winslow Press.

Ulster Folk and Transport Museum
Cultra
Holywood
County Down BT18 0EU
Tel: 028 9042 8428
Fax: 028 9042 8728
Website: www.uftm.org.uk
Memorabilia, reconstructed buildings, sound archive and photographic collections.

Ulster Museum
Botanic Gardens
Belfast BT9 5AB
Tel: 028 9038 3000
Website: www.ulstermuseum.org.uk
Education department collaborates on reminiscence projects, including inter-generational work and loan of reminiscence boxes.

University of Sussex
Centre for Continuing Education
Sussex Institute
Essex House
University of Sussex
Brighton BN1 9QQ
Tel: 01273 877888
Email: si-enquiries@sussex.ac.uk
Website: www.sussex.ac.uk/cce
Information about courses relating to life history, oral history and life story work.

Victoria and Albert Museum (V&A)
Cromwell Road
London SW7 2RL
Tel: 020 7942 2000
Website: www.vam.ac.uk
Undertakes reminiscence work with older learners as part of its education programme.

Your Memories
39 Wallace Avenue
Worthing
West Sussex BN11 5QF
Website: www.yourmemories.co.uk
A free-to-use website and reminiscence database containing thousands of memories and photographs from all over the UK.

About Age Concern

Age Concern is the UK's largest organisation working for and with older people to enable them to make more of life. We are a federation of over 400 independent charities that share the same name, values and standards.

We believe that ageing is a normal part of life, and that later life should be fulfilling, enjoyable and productive. We enable older people by providing services and grants, researching their needs and opinions, influencing government and media, and through other innovative and dynamic projects.

Every day we provide vital services, information and support to thousands of older people of all ages and backgrounds.

Age Concern also works with many older people from disadvantaged or marginalised groups, such as those living in rural areas or older people from black and minority ethnic communities.

Age Concern is dependent on donations, covenants and legacies.

Age Concern England
1268 London Road
London SW16 4ER
Tel: 020 8765 7200
Fax: 020 8765 7211
Website:
www.ageconcern.org.uk

Age Concern Scotland
Causewayside House
160 Causewayside
Edinburgh EH9 1PR
Tel: 0845 833 0200
Fax: 0845 833 0759
Website:
www.ageconcernscotland.org.uk

Age Concern Cymru
Ty John Pathy
Units 13 & 14 Neptune Court
Vanguard Way
Cardiff CF24 5PJ
Tel: 029 2043 1555
Fax: 029 2047 1418
Website: www.accymru.org.uk

Age Concern Northern Ireland
3 Lower Crescent
Belfast BT7 1NR
Tel: 028 9024 5729
Fax: 028 9023 5497
Website: www/ageconcernni.org

Publications from Age Concern Books

Age Concern Books publishes over 65 books, training packs and learning resources aimed at older people, their families, friends and carers, as well as professionals working with and for older people. Publications include:

Your Rights
A guide to money benefits for older people
Sally West

Your Rights has established itself as the money benefits guide for older people. Updated annually, and written in clear, jargon-free language, it ensures that older people – and their advisers – can easily understand the complexities of state benefits and discover the full range of financial support available to them.

For more information, please telephone 0870 44 22 120.

[[Insert other publications. For annuals, don't include ISBN, but as above just:

'[Price] For more information, please telephone 0870 44 22 120.']]

To order from Age Concern Books

Call our hotline: 0870 44 22 120 (for orders or a free books catalogue)

Opening hours 9am–7pm Monday to Friday, 9am–5pm Saturday and Sunday

Books can also be ordered from our secure on-line bookshop: www.ageconcern.org.uk/shop

Alternatively, you can write to Age Concern Books, Units 5 and 6 Industrial Estate, Brecon, Powys LD3 8LA. Fax: 0870 8000 100. Please enclose a cheque or money order for the appropriate amount plus p&p* made payable to Age Concern England. Credit card orders may be made on the order hotline.

*Our postage and packing costs are as follows: mainland UK and Northern Ireland: £1.99 for the first book, 75p for each additional book up to a maximum of £7.50. For customers ordering from outside the mainland UK and NI: credit card payment only; please telephone for international postage rates or email sales@ageconcernbooks.co.uk

Bulk order discounts

Age Concern Books is pleased to offer a discount on orders totalling 50 or more copies of the same title. For details, please contact Age Concern Books on 0870 44 22 120.

Customised editions

Age Concern Books is pleased to offer a free 'customisation' service for anyone wishing to purchase 500 or more copies of most titles. This gives you the option to have a unique front cover design featuring your organisation's logo and corporate colours or to add your logo to the current cover design. You can also insert an additional four pages of text for a small additional fee. Existing clients include many prominent names in British industry, retailing and finance, the trade union movement, educational establishments, public, private and voluntary sectors, and welfare associations. For full details, please contact Sue Henning, Age Concern Books, Astral House, 1268 London Road, London SW16 4ER. Fax: 020 8765 7211. Email: hennins@ace.org.uk

Age Concern Information Line/

Factsheets subscription

Age Concern produces 50 comprehensive factsheets designed to answer many of the questions older people (or those advising them) may have. These include money and benefits, health, community care, leisure and education, and housing. For up to five free factsheets, telephone 0800 00 99 66 (8am–7pm, seven days a week, every week of the year). Alternatively, you may prefer to write to Age Concern, FREEPOST (SWB 30375), ASHBURTON, Devon TQ13 7ZZ.

For professionals working with older people, the factsheets are available on an annual subscription service, which includes updates throughout the year. For further details and costs of the subscription, please contact Age Concern at the above Freepost address.

We hope that this publication has been useful to you. If so, we would very much like to hear from you. Alternatively, if you feel that we could add or change anything, please write and tell us, using the following Freepost address: Age Concern, FREEPOST CN1794, London SW16 4BR.

Index

absenteeism 67, 82–83
activity groups 41
African-Caribbean people 163
    visual conditions 217–218
'Age' 7
Age Exchange Reminiscence
    Centre, Blackheath 16, 140,
    249
age grid, quick reference 60, 61
ageing, views on 3–4
    cultural differences towards
    142–143
aggressive behaviour 22, 46, 77,
    110, 186
Aldridge, David 184
Alzheimer's disease 169–170, 179,
    185
    see also dementia, people with
anxiety 58, 72, 75
Asian people 142
    visual conditions 217–218
    see also Moslems
assessments, care-home 31
asylum seekers see minority ethnic
    elders
Atkinson, Dorothy 226, 228–229,
    230
attitudes to reminiscing 35–37
audio recordings 63, 64, 65, 66,
    118–120, 227
    family history 117
    for PowerPoint life history
    presentations 124
auditory triggers 63, 65, 89–90

autobiographical writing, guided
    21, 104, 106, 107–108,
    205–206
    see also life story books

babies: as triggers 63
Baker, Lorna 236
Bartlett, Liz 163
bearing witness 31, 147–148
Bender, Michael 224
bereavement 199, 235–236
    guidelines for addressing
    238–239
    and people with learning
    disability or dementia 237–
    238
    and reminiscence 239
Birren, B A 109
Birren, J E 107, 108, 109
black/white co-working 149–150
body language 2, 79, 81, 174
Bohlmeijer, E 204
boredom 34, 79, 126
Bornat, Joanna 17, 32
Brenner, T and K 182–183
Brooker, Dawn 176
Brown, A 149
Butler, R 104–105
Butler, Sarah J: *Hearing and Sight
    Loss* 210, 218

camcorders 65, 120
cameras, use of 65
Cappeliez, P 34–35

care homes 17, 21, 85, 101,
147
assessment and care plans 31
design and dementia 178
grief and depression among
residents 111, 202
inter-generational work
154, 165, see also inter-
generational reminiscence
work
key worker system 111
and life story books 115
managers' responsibilities
42–44
personal possessions 206–207
power distribution 29–30
routines and difficult behaviour
111, 191–192
care plans 31, 44, 185, 186
carers
death of 237
domiciliary 17, 101, 245
family 17, 22, 32, 101, 180,
189–190, 245–246
and people with dementia 173,
237, 240–241
and spontaneous reminiscence
101
support needed 173
cassettes/cassette recorders 65,
66
see also audio recordings
cataracts 217
'catastrophic reactions' 192
Causley, John 240
CDs 65, 66, 88, 123, 124
celebrations 84
challenging behaviour, people with
see aggressive behaviour;
difficult behaviour

childhood topics and triggers
93–94
children
and bereavement 236, 238
terminally ill 237
as triggers 63
see also inter-generational
reminiscence work
clearance forms see consent
forms
clothing topics and triggers 95
Cochran, K 107–108
Cocklin, Doreen 227
cognitive behaviour counselling
112
cognitive rehabilitation 192,
193–194
Coleman, Peter 35
collages 117
communication difficulties, people
with, and groupwork 210–
212
see also hearing problems;
language difficulties; speech
problems
community archiving 126
community arts organisations 17,
42
community-based reminiscence
workers 133–134
community development 131–133
and networking 134–135
computer equipment 65, 88
and production of life story
books 120–125, 227–228
confidence, lack of 40–41, 58, 79,
213
confidentiality 44, 66–67
confrontation 82
'confusion' 170–171, 189

see also dementia, people with
consent, obtaining 54
from people with dementia
180–181
see also 'contracting'
consent forms 126, 267, 276
'contracting' 54, 73, 76, 101–102
cooking: as trigger 91–92
Cooper, Mabel 228
cooperation/co-working 42, 43,
48, 49
black and white 149–150
interpreters 151
counselling 36, 81, 112, 205
couple reminiscence 41, 46, 55,
71
phases and stages 39–40
'Crabbit Old Woman, A' 7–9
creative writing groups 109–110
crying 46, 81, 189
Cuijpers, P 204
cultural differences 2, 141–143
see also minority ethnic elders

dance 18, 109
Dauk-Bleess, R 162–163
day centres 17, 21, 85, 101, 118,
154
managers' responsibilities
42–44
and people with dementia 178,
184
deafblind people 210
deafness see hearing problems
death 29, 34, 201, 205
cultural differences towards
141–143
see also bereavement;
terminally ill people
debriefing 49
de Klerk-Rubin, V 195

dementia, people with 29, 51,
148, 168–172
and bereavement and loss
237–238
cognitive rehabilitation 192,
193–194
combining groupwork with other
activities 183
communicating with 173–177,
184–185
and depression 170, 198, 201
and Down's syndrome 231–232
frequency of meetings 56
and gathering life-history details
187–189
groupwork 179–184
involving spouses and partners
189–190
Montessori approach to 182–
183
and multiple sensory problems
210, 211
and music 184–185
obtaining consent 180–181
and places and spaces 178–
179, 191
and reality orientation 192, 193
recording forms for 267,
273–275
Remembering Yesterday, Caring
Today projects 180
specific reminiscence work
185–189
and support for carers 173
when terminally ill 240–241
timing of groupwork 181
using triggers 182, 183–184
validation therapy 192, 193,
194–195
depressed people 200
care-home residents 111, 202

and cherished possessions
206–207
counselling 205
and dementia 170, 198, 201
drug treatment 205
and loss 111, 198–199, 200,
201
reminiscence work with 45–46,
202, 203, 204–205
Deutchman, D 108–109
diabetic retinopathy 217
difficult behaviour 30, 110–111
see also aggressive behaviour
discrimination, racial 28–29, 87,
140, 141, 149, 150, 152
Dobrof, Rose 17
Doka, K J 238
domiciliary carers 17, 101, 245
Down's syndrome, people with
231–232
see also learning disabilities,
people with
drama/drama groups 18, 109
drawing 18, 109
DVDs 65, 66, 88, 124
dying people see terminally ill
people

emotions 19, 75, 80–81, 189
at ending of meetings 83, 84
see also depressed people
employment topics and triggers 96
ethical considerations 125–126
European Reminiscence Network
16, 180, 249
evaluation of project/group 49, 67,
84–85, 247–248
eye contact 174, 175

family carers 17, 22, 32, 101,
189–190, 245–246

training for 180
family history 16, 32, 117
family trees 86, 116, 205
Feil, N 194–195
films, historical 89
finger-spelling 215
Folson, J C 193
food 58–60
and cultural differences 59
as trigger 91–92, 163
Fry, Prem 36
furnishings 178–179

gardens 178
glaucoma 217
Goldsmith, M 173
grandparent projects 164–165
grief/grieving see bereavement;
loss, feelings of
groups/groupwork 16, 20, 21, 28,
40–41
absenteeism 67, 82–83
asking questions 78–79
autobiographical writing 107–
109
beginning phase of meetings
71–77
confidentiality 44, 66–67
for depressed people 204
duration 55
ending phase of meetings
83–85
equipment 64–66
escorting members 57
frequency of meetings 55–56
interviewing members 54–55
invitations 52–53
leadership and staffing 22–23,
42–44, 48–49, 78–80
length and timing of meetings
57, 75–76

location of meetings 56
membership 45–46, 49–50,
  51–52
middle phase of meetings
  77–78, 82
and minority ethnic people *see*
  minority ethnic elders
for people with communication
  problems 210–214
for people with dementia
  179–184
for people with learning
  disabilities 223–224, 225–
  226
and personal memorabilia 82,
  206–207
phases and stages 39–40
record forms/record keeping 66,
  67, 267, 270–275
refreshments 58–60
seating 58, 212, 213
setting objectives 46
size of group 50–51
themes and topics 60–62, 75,
  77, 92–97
use of triggers *see* triggers
Grudzen, M 239
guilt, feelings of 36

Haight, Barbara 105, 106
Harris, Joy 218–219
hearing problems, people with 45,
  51, 210
  amplification aids 211, 215–216
  and groupwork 214–215
Help the Aged: *Recall* 15, 88
Henley, A 33, 59, 142, 146, 150,
  151
Hewitt, Helen 229, 230–231
Hindus 59, 146
history groups, local 16, 41, 63

home life topics and triggers
  94–95
hospitals 17, 21, 50, 56, 84, 85
inter-generational work 154,
  164
managers' responsibilities
  42–44
mental 224–225, 228
hostile behaviour *see* aggressive
  behaviour
housework topics and triggers 95
Hunt, L 148

illness, physical: and loss 200
immigrants *see* minority ethnic
  elders
individual reminiscence work 17,
  20, 41, 45, 51, 55, 71
for people with depression 204
for people with dementia
  185–189
phases and stages 39–40
and planned reminiscence
  101–104
planning and preparation work
  45, 48
record forms 267, 270
and spontaneous reminiscence
  101
using triggers 103
inter-generational reminiscence
  work 22, 31–32, 117
ethnic community groups
  154–155, 163–164
importance of planning and
  preparation 157–158
rewards from 159–162
risk-taking 158–159
teaching skills for living 162–
  163
Internet 65, 66, 88, 122

Internet *(continued)*
and grandparent involvement
164
interpreters, using 151
for deaf people 215
introductions, making 72–73
invitations 51–53

Jewish people 59, 146, 147–148,
205

'Kate – A Crabbit Old Woman' 7–9
Kemp, Mick 15
key workers 52, 111
Killick, John 173, 176–177
'Grass' 178
'You Are Words' 177
Kurland, R 247
Kurokawa, Yukiko 190
KwaZulu-Natal AIDS project 117

Langley, Gordon 15
language difficulties 144, 151
leaders, group 22–23, 42–44,
48–49
black/white 149–150
and ethnic groups 148–149
see also groups/groupwork
League of Jewish Women 147
learning disabilities, people with
and bereavement 237–238
and groupwork 223–224,
225–226
life story work 226–231
leisure topics and triggers 97
Lewy body dementia 170
see also dementia, people with
libraries 17, 42, 63, 66, 93, 134,
136, 244, 245
life reviews 17
evaluative 104–105

structured 20, 21, 23, 29,
105–107, 202
and terminally ill people 237
life stories 17, 22
audio tape recordings 118–120
and computer technology
120–125
and property rights 67–68
storyboards 118
using to illuminate present
behaviour 110–111
video recordings 120
see also life story books
life story books 103–104, 115,
116
and family trees 116
of people with learning
disabilities 226–231
lip-reading classes 215
loss, feelings of 80–81, 111,
198–200, 235–236
of people with learning disability
or dementia 224–225,
237–238
Lynn, L E 144

McConkey, J 37
McKee, K 43
macular degeneration 217
managers 42–44
Marshall, Mary 148, 178
memorabilia 82, 117, 206–207
memory 37
loss of 171–172
memory boxes 117
Microsoft PowerPoint life story
presentations 122–125
mime 18, 109, 214
minority ethnic elders 33, 52
acquiring background
knowledge of 139–140

bearing witness 147–148
benefits from sharing
    recollections 140–141
differences in responses 2,
    141–145
and food 59
and hearing problems 215
inter-generational reminiscence
    work 154–155, 163–164
language difficulties 144, 151
and leadership and staffing of
    groups 140, 148–150
learning from 145–147
and racial discrimination 28–29,
    87, 140, 141, 149, 150, 152
religious festivals 146
Mistry, T 149
morale: and types of reminiscers
    35–37
mosaics 117
Moslems 59, 86–87, 146
Mothers' Living Stories Project
    236
murals 117
museums 17, 42, 60, 63, 93, 134,
    136, 244, 245
music 18, 109
and people with dementia
    184–185
and terminally ill people 238
as trigger 63, 89–90
see also singing
Muslims see Moslems
'mutual aid' groups 40–41

names, use of 72
National Vocational Qualifications
    (NVQs) 249–250
networking 134–135
newspapers and magazines 21,
    63, 88, 184

noisy people 110, 191–192
non-verbal communication 2, 81,
    86, 174, 195
Northen, H 247
Northern Ireland Film and
    Television Commission 88
NVQs (National Vocational
    Qualifications) 249–250

'obsessive' reminiscences 46, 112
Open College 249
Open University 250–251
oral history 15, 16, 17, 32, 41
compared with reminiscence
    129, 130–131
South African projects 159
O'Rourke, N 34–35
outings 20, 84, 226
ownership rights 67–68

painful recollections 19, 21, 33,
    42, 80–81, 142, 203
painting 18, 109
parties, farewell 84
Pear, T 19
personal history forms 54, 267,
    268–269
personal possessions 82, 206–
    207
pet animals: as triggers 63
photographs 117
and life story books 116
for PowerPoint life history
    presentations 123–124
as triggers 65, 86–88, 103,
    206, 225
Pickles, W 238
Pierce, Tom 123, 124
poems
    'Age' 7
    'Grass' 178

poems *(continued)*
'Kate – A Crabbit Old Woman'
7–9
'You Are Words' 177
poetry/poetry groups 18, 86,
109–110, 219–220
PowerPoint life story presentations
122–125
problem-solving, reminiscence as
146, 147
projectors, use of 64–65
property rights 67–68
psychotherapy 42, 81, 205
publication of life stories 67–68,
227–228

questions, asking 78–79
quilts 117

racism 28–29, 87, 140, 141, 149,
150, 152
radio 89, 90
Read, Peter 143
reality orientation (RO) 192, 193
record-keeping 66, 67
forms for 67, 267–276
refreshments 58–60
refugees *see* minority ethnic elders
religious festivals 146
Remembering Yesterday, Caring
Today projects 180
reminiscence/reminiscence work
1–2, 5–6, 10
characteristics 18–19, 107
compared with oral history 129,
130–131
definitions 13–14
functions 26–35
general and specific 21–22
history of 15–18
reluctance to participate in 19,
33, 35, 36, 111, 148

skills needed 22–23
as therapy 20, 42
repetitiveness 112
research, need for 246–247
resource materials 63–64, 244–
245
see also triggers
retinitis pigmentosa 217
reviewing reminiscence work 49,
84–85
RO (reality orientation) 192, 193
routines: and difficult behaviour
111, 191–192
Rowlings, C 148
RYCT (Remembering Yesterday,
Caring Today projects) 180

scapegoats 78
school-based projects *see* inter-
generational reminiscence
work
schooldays topics and triggers
94
Schott, J 33, 59, 142, 146, 150,
151
Schweitzer, Pam 140, 155,
159–161, 164
Scottish Vocational Qualifications
(SVQs) 249–250
sessional contracting 76
SHAP calendar 146
Sherman, E 206
Shulman, L 40
shy people 72, 77
sight loss, people with 51, 210,
217
groupwork with 216, 217–218
visual aids 218
sign languages 215
Sikhs: and food 59
silent people 77, 81
singing 90, 184, 185, 220

smells: as triggers 63, 91
Smit, F 204
Social Care Councils 250, 251
Soltys, F G 239
sound triggers 65, 89–90
South African oral history projects
   159
speech problems, people with 45,
   51, 210
   and groupwork 218–220
spontaneous reminiscence 101
staff responsibilities and roles
   42–44, 48–49, 185–186
Stelson, C 162–163
storyboards 118
Sussex, University of 251
SVQs (Scottish Vocational
   Qualifications) 249–250

tactile triggers 90, 214
tapes see audio recordings
'task-centred' groups 41
tastes: as triggers 91
Taulbee, L R 193
tearfulness 46, 81, 189
terminally ill people 236–237
   carers of 237
   children 237
   mothers 236
   and music 238
   people with dementia 240–241
   and reminiscence 239
themes and topics 60–62, 75, 77,
   92–97
Thompson, Paul 32
time lines 116
training, reminiscence 22, 180,
   246, 248–251
triggers, using 21, 62, 63–64, 75,
   77, 79, 86
   auditory 63, 65, 89–90

cherished objects 82, 206–207
commercial packages 64, 88
and individual reminiscence
   work 103
for minority ethnic elders
   145–146
multi-sensory 213, 214
for people with dementia 182,
   183–184
for people with learning
   disabilities 225, 226
smells 63, 91
tactile 90, 214
tastes 91
use of too many 79
visual 63–64, 86–89, 218
Tuckman, B W 40

university courses 250–251

validation therapy 192, 193,
   194–195
Van Dongen, Els 159
vascular dementia 170
   see also dementia, people with
video recordings 65, 120
visual problems see sight loss,
   people with
visual triggers 63–64, 86–89, 218
volunteers 17, 22, 136, 245
   minority ethnic 151

wallhangings 117
wartime topics and triggers 96–97
Webster, Jeffrey D 203, 209
   Reminiscence Functions Scale
   34
wills, making 206
Woods, R T 204–205
work topics and triggers 96
writing groups 109–110

Age Concern Books

Age Concern publishes over 65 books, training packs and learning resources aimed at older people, their families, friends and carers, as well as professionals working with and for older people.

For a **free books catalogue** showing all our titles, telephone our hotline: 0870 44 22 120.

To order a book:

- Telephone our hotline: **0870 44 22 120**
  (Opening hours: 9am-7pm Mon to Fri, 9am-5pm Sat and Sun)

- Website: **www.ageconcern.org.uk/bookshop** (secure online bookshop)

- Post: send a cheque or money order to:
  Age Concern Books, Units 5 and 6 Industrial Estate, Brecon, Powys LD3 8LA. Fax: 0870 8000 100. Cheques payable to Age Concern England for the appropriate amount plus p&p.

Postage and packing: mainland UK and Northern Ireland: £1.99 for the first book, 75p for each additional book up to a maximum of £7.50. For customers ordering from outside the mainland UK and NI: credit card payment only; please telephone for international postage rates or email sales@ageconcernbooks.co.uk

Bulk order discounts are available on orders totalling 50 or more copies of the same title. For details, please contact Age Concern Books on 0870 44 22 120.

Free service for businesses and organisations: for orders totalling 500 or more copies of the same title, you can have a unique front cover design featuring your organisation's logo and corporate colours, or adding your logo to the current cover design. You can also insert an additional four pages of text for a small additional fee. For full details, please contact Beth Vaughan, Age Concern Books, Astral House, 1268 London Road, London SW16 4ER. Fax: 020 8765 7211. Email: books@ace.org.uk

Age Concern Factsheets

Age Concern produces 45 comprehensive factsheets designed to answer many of the questions older people (or those advising them) may have. These include money and benefits, health, community care, leisure and education, and housing. For up to five free factsheets, telephone the information line on 0800 00 99 66 (8am-7pm, seven days a week, every week of the year). Alternatively you may prefer to download them free from our website: www.ageconcern.org.uk

Cross Cultural Care

Culture, Religion and Patient Care in a Multi-Ethnic Society:
A handbook for professionals
Alix Henley and Judith Schott

Meeting cultural and religious needs is an essential part of providing care in a multi-ethnic society. This book describes ways of identifying individual needs and offers sensitive and practical approaches to adapting care to meet them. It is rooted in the experiences and views of people of minority cultural and religious groups.

'...a stimulating and accessible book that is a useful introduction for the healthcare professional to explore how best to meet the healthcare needs of a multi-ethnic society.' Nursing Standard

The book is an important and invaluable resource for everyone involved in providing, planning or managing care in hospitals, in the community, in residential care, and in hospices. Its wealth of references make it ideal for undergraduate and postgraduate students.

£19.99 + p&p   0-86242-231-0
                                                         624 pages

Cross Cultural Care:
A training pack to use with care assistants
working with older people in all care settings
Helen Howard

This pack provides an introduction to the principles of cross cultural care for older people through engaging participants in thinking about their own experience, identity and lifestyles. It will help care providers to meet their responsibilities under the Care Standards Act 2000 to train care staff, and to meet the national minimum standards for their service. A wide range of topics covered include:

- Racial, ethnic and cultural identity
- The changing nature of cultures
- Understanding prejudice and discrimination
- Issues around touch and privacy

Learning is achieved through interactive methods, including discussion of case studies and small group activities. Each session has support material, including overhead transparencies and photocopiable handouts.

£35 + p&p   0-86242-355-4
                                  Ring binder cover. Contains 74 pages
                                  and 17 key point overhead transparencies

Care Professional Handbook Series

Hearing and Sight Loss
Sarah Butler

Although a sensory impairment may not be life-threatening in itself, it can exacerbate other impairments and contribute to a major loss of independence for older people. This in-depth handbook offers an holistic approach, bringing together information on the different sensory impairments (visual, hearing and dual impairment). It explores the ways in which sensory impairment affects older people in the care system, and offers a wide range of ways to support them.

£14.99 + p&p   0-86242-359-7

Money at Home: The home care worker's guide to handling other people's finances and belongings
Pauline Thompson

This guide covers some of the key issues to consider when handling other people's money and belongings. It is essential reading for: home care workers, and staff and volunteers who visit people in their own homes in an official capacity and who may be involved in assisting with some financial matters; home care managers, who are responsible for devising procedures on the handling of money and belongings.

£7.99 + p&p   0-86242-293-0

■ This book reflects the law and practice in England. However, many of the principles are similar across the UK.

Nutritional Care for Older People: A guide to good practice
June Copeman

Food plays a vital role in all of our lives, but can present a particular challenge for those looking after older people. A sound, balanced diet, and appetising meals can have a major impact on their health, well-being, and general motivation. Packed full of practical information and guidance, this book will help staff develop and maintain the very best good practice in all aspects of nutritional care.

£14.99 + p&p   0-86242-284-1

Older people: Assessment for health and social care
Hazel Heath and Roger Watson

480 pages packed with essential information. Assessment is the foundation for health and social care, and integral to all areas of policy and practice with older people. This book aims to support assessment for health and social care, in all its diversity, by offering a knowledge base to underpin assessment practice and the decisions that result from this.

£16.99 + p&p   0-86242-376-7

Other Titles for Care Professionals

Accident Prevention in Residential and Nursing Homes
Royal Society for the Prevention of Accidents (RoSPA)

£45 + p&p   0-86242-402-X
                                             Ring binder cover

Alive and Kicking: The carer's guide to exercises for older people
Julie Sobczak

£11.99 + p&p   0-86242-289-2

Counselling and Older People: An introductory guide
Edited by Verena Tschudin

£12.99 + p&p   0-86242-245-0

Reminiscence Trainer's Pack
For use in health, housing, social care and arts organisations; colleges, libraries and museums; volunteers' and carers agencies
Faith Gibson

£35 + p&p   0-86242-305-8
                                             Shrink-wrapped product

Their Rights: Advance directives and living wills explored
Kevin Kendrick and Simon Robinson

£9.99 + p&p   0-86242-244-2

The Successful Activity Co-ordinator
For activity and care staff engaged in developing an active care home
Rosemary Hurtley and Jennifer Wenborn

£25 + p&p   0-86242-390-2
                                             Ring binder cover

Trained Nurse's Teaching Packs
For use in the workplace to educate nursing auxiliaries, health care assistants and social services care staff
Gill Early and Sarah Miller

Volume 1   £35 + p&p   0-86242-357-0
Volume 2   £35 + p&p   0-86242-400-3
                                             Ring binder covers

Understanding Bereavement Training Pack
A guide for carers working with older people
Toni Battison

£35 + p&p   0-86242-304-X
                                             Shrink-wrapped product

Dementia

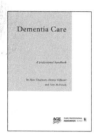

Dementia Care:
A handbook for residential and day care
Alan Chapman, Donna Gilmour and Iain McIntosh

This revised edition stresses the holistic approach to the support of people with dementia in residential and day care. Topics include: the individual and their previous lifestyle; what is dementia; health matters; behaviour as a response to the living environment; behaviour as a response to the daily routine and staff actions; feelings of loss, pain and palliative care; issues for day care; and staff teamwork.

£14.99 + p&p   0-86242-313-9

Introducing Dementia:
The essential facts and issues of care
David Sutcliffe

This book is an introductory guide to the whole field of dementia, particularly as it manifests itself in today's society. Stressing the importance of person-centred care, which emphasises physical, emotional, psychological and spiritual care, this book helps raise awareness and improve standards.

£14.99 + p&p   0-86242-283-3

Promoting Mobility for People with Dementia:
A problem-solving approach
Rosemary Oddy

The second edition of this popular book outlines common sense approaches for enabling people with dementia to move and remain mobile, without jeopardising the health and safety of those who care for them. The key problems associated with mobility are identified and suggestions given on how to address them.

£14.99 + p&p   0-86242-361-9

Supporting People with Dementia:
A training pack for staff development
Dementia Voice

This training pack is an ideal resource for developing staff knowledge; values and skills in caring for people with dementia in care homes or day care settings. The training sessions are interactive to build on the existing skills and knowledge of course participants and to reflect the diverse experience and learning styles.

£45 + p&p   0-86242-349-X
Ring binder cover